DEVIL BIRDS

DEVIL BIRDS
The Life of the Swift

Derek Bromhall

Hutchinson
London Melbourne Sydney Auckland Wellington Johannesburg

Acknowledgements

It is a pleasure to acknowledge the help I have received in writing and illustrating this book.

In common with all who study the life of the swift I owe a debt of gratitude to the late Dr David Lack, FRS, and his wife Elizabeth, whose publications have contributed so much to our knowledge. It was Dr Lack who, in 1948, installed the nestboxes in the roof of the Tower of Oxford University's Museum of Science to accommodate what has since become the best known colony of swifts in the world. Dr Lack's successor as Director of the Edward Grey Institute of Field Ornithology, Dr Christopher Perrins, is also an authority on swifts, and I would like to thank him for the help he has given since the idea of making a film on the swifts was first conceived. To the Committee for the Scientific Collections of the Museum of Science and the staff of the Museum my thanks are due for their courtesy in permitting us to work in the Tower and in accommodating so many visits at such odd times.

In compiling material for this book I am particularly indebted to Roy Overall for information and data on the swifts nesting in the Tower; to Chris Mead, of the British Trust for Ornithology, for providing me with the latest records of recoveries of swifts ringed in Britain; and to Dr Martin Speight for analysing the composition of meals fed to the nestlings. Dr Bruce Campbell has kindly read through the text and his comments have been most welcome, coming as they do from an authority whose knowledge of birds is encyclopaedic.

The photographs are individually acknowledged at the end of the book, but I would like to add my special thanks for the major contributions made by my colleague Tony Allen and my son Clive. Both spent countless hours in the Tower and have produced some outstanding photographs.

Having now written a book and made a film about swifts I feel very much in their debt, a feeling which must be shared by others who have been privileged to study wild animals at close quarters. In special cases it may be possible to go some way towards repaying this debt directly, for instance where effective measures to save a species or its habitat may follow the appearance of a book or film; but in most instances repayment is indirect, with benefits accruing to wildlife in general.

In the case of the swift it might be supposed that its life is so remote from ours that our influence on it must be minimal. But almost unawares we have been providing swifts with nest sites in the roofs of our homes for centuries; equally unwittingly we may be denying future generations of swifts their traditional sites, as new buildings replace old and roof spaces are sealed off to conserve heat. The swift is in fact in greater potential danger now than at any time in the past.

To counteract this we should now be installing nestboxes for swifts wherever this is feasible. There can be few birds as beneficial to man as the swift and certainly no greater scourge of insects. And for those who take the trouble and have the patience to establish their own colony, there will be the immeasurable reward of being able to observe, enjoy and discover for themselves what it is about the swift that makes it the most fascinating and challenging of all birds.

Derek Bromhall
Oxford
March 1980

Contents

1

Of all the birds that have achieved mastery of the air in their individual ways, none is so specialized for an aerial existence as the European, or common, swift *Apus apus*. It spends almost its entire life on the wing, flying continuously, day and night for months or even years at a time. Unless forced down by accident or by bad weather and cold it stops flying only when it has found a place in which to nest.

A swift obtains everything it needs from the air; food in the form of insects, water as rain or taken on the wing from lake or river, and nest materials borne on the wind. It 'sleeps' on the wing by flying high into the sky at sunset and riding the air currents all night. Swifts even mate on the wing, surely the ultimate adaptation to a completely aerial existence. As a group swifts are the fastest of all birds in level flight, and the needle-tailed swifts of Africa and Asia have been reported to attain speeds of up to 170 k.p.h. (105 m.p.h.).

For a bird weighing a mere 40–50 grams (1½ ounces) the European swift has an exceptionally long life-span, averaging about five and a half years. Most of our common song-birds, some of them much larger than a swift, may be expected to live no more than two years. A swift found dying in Oxford in 1964 was wearing a ring placed on its leg sixteen years previously, when it was already adult and so at least two, and probably three, years of age. When it died this bird must have been eighteen or more years old, and it has been calculated that in its lifetime it flew a distance of some 4 million miles, equivalent to flying to the moon and back eight times.

European swifts spend most of the year in southern Africa, but each spring they migrate to Europe as far north as Lapland, inside the Arctic Circle, and eastwards to China, to nest and rear their young.

The best known colony of swifts nest in the Tower of Oxford University's Museum of Science

During the summer, swifts may be seen in their thousands wheeling and darting in the air over towns and villages. On a fine, warm day a faint scream coming out of a clear sky tells us that the swifts are flying high, and by straining the eyes one can discern the tiny, black crescent-winged birds scything through the air as they hawk for insects. When clouds blot out the sun and the air is chilled and damp the swifts fly low and are silent; as they flash past with flickering wings they reveal themselves as small compact birds, entirely black except for a pale throat, and with narrow curved wings so long as to seem out of proportion to their bodies.

On bright summer mornings and in the evenings an hour or so before sunset, parties of swifts indulge in displays of aerobatics, over roof-tops and around towers and chimneys and trees, which for sheer speed and virtuosity are unrivalled by any other bird. From time to time several in a party scream together as they swoop low, creating a sound like no other, shrill and loud enough to be heard even above traffic noise.

Although the sight and sounds of swifts are commonplace throughout Europe during the summer months, from May to August, the birds themselves are unapproachable. When not flying they hide away completely in dark

The supreme specialist in fast sustained flight; the swift's long curved wings will keep it airborne for years, but its legs have become almost useless

recesses in the roofs of old buildings. They do not perch on trees or hop on the ground, like other birds, nor are their young ever seen, as are those of birds that leave the nest as ungainly fledglings, protected and fed by the parents until able to fly properly and fend for themselves.

Little wonder that swifts have long been birds of mystery, and the subject of legend and folklore. In England the swift used to be called the Develing, Devil's screech, Skir devil, or Devil's bird; it is easy to imagine a pack of swifts, small black projectiles, hurtling from the sky at a phenomenal speed and screaming like banshees, as a fistful of little demons flung by the Devil, returning at nightfall to some Satanic roosting place.

Before bird migration was accepted as a fact, swifts, swallows and other birds that disappeared at the end of summer were thought to hibernate through the winter. In the sixteenth century swallows were even believed to spend the winter cocooned in the mud at the bottom of lakes, a legend which appears to have been originated by Olaus Magnus, Bishop of Uppsala, in Sweden, and which persisted for two centuries. In the middle of the eighteenth century, when it was recognized that some birds migrated to warmer countries for the winter, swifts and swallows were still thought to hibernate. Even Gilbert White, the great eighteenth-century British naturalist, while speculating on the possibility of swifts and swallows migrating, nevertheless employed men to dig in places where the birds were thought likely to hibernate. Although aware that swallows, evidently wearied by travel, were commonly seen on the Continent in the autumn, White seems to have clung to the legend that they hibernate, as indeed did the great Swedish taxonomist Linnaeus.

Legends and folklore about wildlife, however improbable, are believed with extraordinary readiness and may even be supported by supposed eye-witness testimony. Only slowly, and with some resistance, are they displaced by real facts. Even today there are those who believe that bats seek out women's hair in which to become entangled, that nightjars suck milk from goats, and that adders swallow their own young to protect them from danger.

The first convincing evidence that swifts migrate was provided by another eighteenth-century naturalist, Edward Jenner, who is better known for demonstrating the efficacy of vaccination against disease. By cutting off some of the toes of several swifts he caught at the nest he was able to recognize them when they returned in subsequent springs; and because these birds were fit and healthy on their arrival

9

Swifts have probably nested in the roof of this Elizabethan cottage at Henley-on-Thames for over 400 years.

Above: A typical swift nest, under the rafters

Left: Access to the nest in this Victorian house is via the eaves, with a clear flight path below

he argued that they must have been feeding during the winter and not hibernating.

With the realization that birds migrate between Europe and the tropics the mystery of why they disappear in the autumn gave way to the greater mystery of where they go, how they navigate and what factors determine the time and pattern of migration, questions to which even now the answers are incomplete. Indeed, bird migration, now being investigated on a global scale, has become one of the most challenging and complex studies in biology. Birds are remarkable pathfinders and utilize senses of which we are only imperfectly aware: they possess an internal clock and sun and star compasses; they can detect changes of barometric pressure; they employ the earth's magnetic field and possibly also its gravitational field; they use the senses of smell, sight – including an ability to perceive polarized and ultraviolet light – and hearing sensitive enough to detect infrasound. To complicate matters further, the ways in which particular birds respond to the drive to migrate varies with species, sex, age, experience, geographical location, season and weather. Yet the study of bird migration is still in its infancy; for not a single species is the entire uninterrupted route of its migration known.

Of all the birds that migrate to Africa from Europe and Asia the swift is the one about which we know least. A major problem is identification; Africa has many resident swifts, of several species, very similar in appearance and difficult to identify on the wing. The African black swift *Apus barbatus*, in particular, is almost impossible to distinguish from the European swift in the air. Although a few specimens of European swifts had been positively identified in southern Africa in the 1950s it was not until 1960 that the first British ringed swift was recovered, in Zaire. Between 1960 and 1978, twenty-three swifts ringed in Britain have been recovered in Malawi, Mozambique, Zimbabwe-Rhodesia, Tanzania, Zaire, and Zambia (see map on page 82). A bird ringed in Yorkshire on 19 July 1962, and recovered five months later, on 29 December, in Zimbabwe-Rhodesia, 9000 kilometres (5600 miles) away, has set the southernmost limit to the distribution of the common swift at the present time at 20° 10′ S, 30° 49′ E.

Over the years the life story of the swift has slowly been pieced together through the efforts of amateur naturalists as well as professional ornithologists, and the truth about this extraordinary bird is revealed as much stranger than any legend.

11

The weathering of centuries has formed crevices between the stones of this ancient church tower, allowing the swifts access to the interior (*courtesy:* Lord Saye and Sele)

The greatest contribution to our knowledge of the swift was made by the late Dr David Lack. While Director of the Edward Grey Institute of Field Ornithology at Oxford University, Dr Lack, with his wife Elizabeth, spent years studying the colony of swifts which nest in the Tower of the University Museum, and in 1956 the results of this study, together with a review of the world's swifts, were published in a book entitled *Swifts in a Tower*. This is now a classic, beautifully written by an authority who devoted his life to the study of birds.

In 1975, when I decided to make a film on the life of the swift, I drew heavily on the wealth of information contained in *Swifts in a Tower* and in recognition of my debt to David Lack I was happy to dedicate the film *Devil Birds* to his memory.

My own involvement with swifts, or rather a frustrated lack of involvement, goes back to the time when, as a boy hunting for birds' nests in the lovely Shropshire countryside, I had first become acquainted with 'Jacky Squealers', as the local boys called them. I was intrigued by a bird whose nest I never found and frustrated at not being able to include its eggs in my treasured collection. The only clue we boys ever had as to where swifts were nesting was when a swift dived out of the sky and disappeared into a tiny crevice between the stones in the tower of an ancient church, without apparently checking its speed for an instant.

It was not until many years later, when I climbed the ladders in the roof of the Museum Tower at Oxford, that I first saw the eggs I had so coveted as a boy. This was long after my collecting days were over, when the urge to acquire and label, be they birds' eggs or butterflies, had given way to a desire to capture the lives of wild creatures on film. Since that first visit, I have spent many hours in the Tower, over a period of several years, watching and filming the swifts of that same colony that Dr Lack studied, from their arrival in May until the departure of the young birds in August.

No single medium of communication is adequate in itself to portray a life story, certainly not one as fascinating as that of the swift. Perhaps the most satisfactory is the documentary film, in which wild animals can be seen, close up and in great detail, behaving normally in their natural habitats. But a film, made within very rigid constraints of structure and time, must leave out much that is interesting but not visually exciting. Also, the involvement of the photographer must be subordinated, or preferably completely excluded, as an unwanted intrusion into the lives of the animals being filmed.

Like anyone privileged to study swifts over a long period and at close range, I have become very involved with these incredible birds, an involvement which finds expression in this book. In writing it I am keenly aware of my limitations; although I can fairly describe myself as a biologist, in its widest interpretation, I do not pretend to be an ornithologist. But having spent several summers observing and recording on film the life story of the swifts that live in the Tower I am happy to include myself among the many naturalists, amateurs and professional, who have been so fascinated by the swift that they have felt compelled to tell others of what they have seen.

When filming wild creatures it is essential to understand them well enough to be able to anticipate what they will do next, and in acquiring this understanding, which takes a long time, it not infrequently happens that observations are made which have eluded even the experts.

Paradoxically, although the swift actually lives with us under our roofs, its way of life makes it remote and unapproachable, and so it does not receive the attention, or the affection, lavished on blue tits and robins and other of our garden birds that we can feed and which entertain us at close quarters throughout the year. But even swifts can be brought nearer, through the camera and in the pages of a book; and familiarity with them can only breed greater respect. Of one thing we can be sure, no matter how much we may learn about the swift the mystery that has always surrounded it will continue to do so; it is the nature of the mystery that will change.

13

2

The European or common swift is but one of many species of swifts, distributed worldwide, which exhibit an extraordinary array of adaptations. As a group they must pose the greatest challenge to the ornithologist. Fascinating though they are, they have been little studied, and for good reason. All fly like frenzied bullets, are easily confused with one another in the air, and nest in sites which are at best difficult of access and at worst impossible.

The alpine swift *Apus melba* and the pallid swift *Apus pallidus* of Europe and the Mediterranean, as well as many African species and the western American white-throated swift *Aeronautes saxatilis,* nest in crevices in cliff faces chosen for their inaccessibility.

The cloud or collared swift *Cypseloides zonaris* of South America attains total protection from predators by selecting cliffs behind waterfalls on which to roost at night and lay its eggs. Among the most awesome sights in Nature are the Iguazu Falls, where Brazil, Argentina and Paraguay meet. They form a 4-kilometre (2½-mile) horseshoe of raging water four times the span of Niagara Falls and 88 metres (287 feet) high. The main channel spills through a gorge called the Devil's Throat, over which a permanent cloud of mist and spray rises 150 metres (500 feet) into the air, and behind a wall of water the cloud swifts nest and rear their young. To reach the cliff face they dive down the falling water, through the spray, and when their speed matches the velocity of the water they dart through a break in the torrent and cling to the saturated rocks behind. An impregnable refuge, but one can only wonder at what price! The young swift, plunging from its nest on the cliff face and taking to the air for the first time, has only one chance of penetrating an almost solid wall of water to reach the outside world; natural selection at its most demanding.

The Old and New World palm swifts belonging to the genera *Cypsiurus* and *Tachornis* and Asian crested swifts *Hemiprocne* nest high up in trees, using saliva to cement their eggs, as well as their nests, to palm leaves or tree branches.

The Asian crested swift, despite its large size, makes the smallest nest, a few feathers and fragments of plant material formed into a cup, stuck to a branch, and just large enough to contain a single egg. The egg is also cemented in place with saliva. During incubation the swift sits perched across the branch so that its brood-patch is in contact with the egg, the bird's weight being supported by its legs.

The most elaborate nests are made by the tropical American scissor-tailed swifts *Panyptila.* Suspended from an overhanging rock or branch and constructed of wind-borne plant seeds or feathers cemented together by saliva, the nest is substantial enough to be used in successive years. An opening at the base leads into a vertical tube, and at its inner end is a ledge on which the eggs are laid. This design is common to other birds, such as weavers, oropendulas and forest flycatchers, at risk from snakes, mocking birds, jays and other predators. Like the European swift and the American chimney swift, scissor-tailed swifts have taken to man-made structures, and their nests can be seen hanging under the arches of buildings throughout Central America. In the ancient Mayan capital of Tical, deep in the Guatemalan jungle, I once climbed to the top of the ruin of Temple IV, towering above even the tallest trees, and stood in a recess where centuries ago Mayan priests had officiated at ceremonies in which humans were horribly sacrificed; above my head hung the nest of a scissor-tailed swift.

The majority of swifts are highly secretive in their choice of nest sites, and commonly seek

The Iguazu Falls, home of the Cloud Swift

out dark recesses or holes. The Horus swift of Africa nests in the burrows of martins, excavated in cliffs of sand. The large group of spine-tailed swifts *Chaetura*, found in America, Africa and Asia, commonly attach their bracket-like nests by saliva to the inside of hollow trees. The giant swift of Malaysia, largest of the spine-tailed group, also nests in hollow trees, placing the nest in the debris at the bottom of the hole.

The American chimney swift *Chaetura pelagica,* as its name implies, has taken to chimneys, the man-made equivalent of hollow trees, as nesting sites and as roosts outside the breeding season. The cup-shaped nest is made of twigs, cemented to the inside of the chimney with saliva, and to gather nest material the chimney swift snaps off small twigs with its toes as it flies over the tops of trees, a remarkable feat for a bird weighing less than an ounce.

Chimneys and hollow trees are used as overnight roosts by huge numbers of chimney swifts on their winter migration to South America. Over a century ago John James Audubon, the great American naturalist and illustrator, discovered some 9000 swifts clinging to the inside of a huge sycamore tree and more recently over 12,000 birds have been counted in a single chimney.

The swiftlets of the Himalayas and South-East Asia prefer even larger holes. In the Himalayas colonies of swiftlets nest in limestone potholes more than 60 metres (200 feet) deep, in almost total darkness. The most famous swiftlets are those which provide the raw material for birds' nest soup. In Borneo, in particular, enormous colonies of swiftlets of the genus *Collocalia* attach their nests, made almost entirely of saliva, to the walls and roofs of huge caves. The best known of these are the Niah caves, with a population of swiftlets estimated at over a million. Each season tens of thousands of their nests are taken and sold, mainly to Chinese traders, birds' nest soup being highly esteemed among the Chinese community, even though birds' saliva has little nutritive value.

The swiftlets exhibit yet another adaptation to a highly specialized way of life. In the caves, where no light penetrates, the swiftlets find their way about, locating their nests and avoiding collisions with other birds, by echo-location. Clicks emitted during flight are reflected back to the bird and interpreted to give a mental picture of its surroundings, a method similar to the ultra-sonic system of echo-location which has evolved in bats. As the clicks of the swiftlets are audible to the human ear the noise in the caves can be almost deafening. How each individual bird, among the tens of thousands in the air at the same time, can distinguish its own sound emissions and echoes from the others is a mystery.

There are in all some seventy species of swifts distributed throughout the world, but few undertake long-distance breeding migrations to cool Northern Temperate latitudes. The European swift, which spends the greater part of the year in southern Africa, returns to Europe and Asia for the short summer breeding season; the alpine swift nests in Switzerland and winters in Zaire; the northern race of the Pacific white-rumped swift *Apus pacificus* and the Asian needle-tailed swifts winter in Australasia but nest in Siberia, China and Japan; the chimney swift breeds in eastern North America but spends the winter in South America; while Vaux and black swifts *Cypseloides* of western North America migrate to Central America.

The reason why these species should all fly south in the autumn is clear enough; there is insufficient insect food to sustain them during the northern winter, even if they could withstand the cold. But the reasons why they should ever leave a tropical climate and fly north in the spring are not so apparent; the majority of the world's swifts live in the tropics, obtaining all their needs and breeding successfully without undergoing such migrations.

Since all migrating species of swift fly north to breed there must be advantages in rearing the offspring in a temperate climate. This is true of course for many species of birds other than swifts; a host of summer migrants breed in the cooler latitudes, taking advantage of the seasonal abundance of insects as food for their young. However, for the European swift the advantages seem marginal. The migration

To reach the cliff face,
where they build their
nests and roost at night,
Cloud Swifts must fly
through a torrent of water

Palm Swifts attach their nests and eggs to the underside of palm leaves with saliva. When the chick hatches, it must grip the nest very tightly to withstand the buffeting of the wind

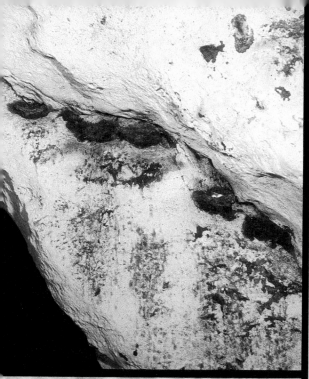

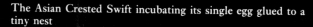
The Asian Crested Swift incubating its single egg glued to a tiny nest

The swiftlets, *Collocalia*, build nests almost entirely of saliva, which are harvested to make 'birds' nest' soup. *salangana* in the Niah Great Cave, Sarawak *fuciphaga unicolor*, the Indian edible nest swift

ight: The nest of a Scissor-tailed Swift, hanging in a cess in Temple IV, Tical, Guatemala

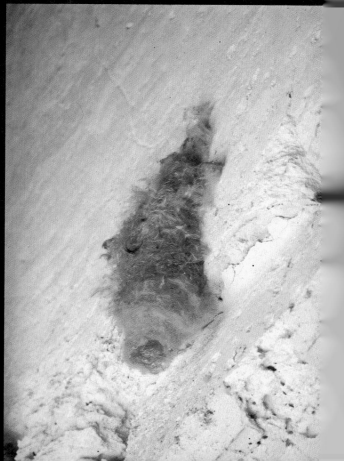

The American Chimney
Swift cements its nest of
twigs to the inside of a
chimney or hollow tree

itself is very hazardous to the adults, not so much because of the distance travelled – a journey of around 6000 miles presents no great problems of endurance to a bird which may fly 500 miles or more in a single day to avoid a region of bad weather – but because the route followed takes the migrating swifts through regions where cold, rain and high winds may force them down or weaken them so that they fall victim to a predator such as the hobby, a small falcon which will take swifts slowed down by fatigue. In very bad weather at night swifts may cluster together for warmth on the walls of buildings, clinging on to rough surfaces by their backward-pointing claws; those on the outside of the cluster may well die of exposure during the night, and if any fall to the ground their chances of survival are virtually nil.

Once the swifts are back in Europe or Asia the success or failure of the breeding season is determined by the vagaries of the weather. In a fine warm summer an abundance of insects ensures good survival of the broods, but even in an average summer there are periods of rain and cold winds which result in reduced clutch size and the survival of fewer chicks. In the appalling English summer of 1954, when the weather was continuously cold and wet, food was so scarce that in the Tower twenty-five pairs of adults reared only fourteen chicks; in a tower in Devon where a colony has been studied for many years, all the chicks of that year starved to death and even the adults were so weak that they could only lie feebly in the hand when lifted from the nest.

Good summers in Europe are infrequent enough to be memorable and yet every year the swifts return to breed, whatever the weather. Over the many thousands of years during which the pattern of migration has become established, the benefit to the species of a plentiful supply of insects, normally available to the swifts during the long days of the northern summer, must outweigh the disadvantages and hazards of migration and the vicissitudes of weather.

A curious feature of the annual migration of the swift is that it is not only the breeding adults

A European Swift, forced down by bad weather and starvation, clings to the rough surface of a wall, too weak to fly; each foot has four backward-pointing claws acting as hooks.

which make the journey. Immature birds also return to Europe, though they may not breed successfully until they are four years old. Even though the breeding adults need additional food during the summer for their chicks, the non-breeding swifts have only themselves to feed, and it would seem improbable that they migrate to Europe because there are insufficient insects in Africa to sustain them the year round. Nor do they need to accompany the breeding adults to Europe to learn the route; on the outward journey to Africa the newly fledged swifts leave Europe ahead of their parents and are guided to their destination by instinct, as are the young of other summer migrants, notably the cuckoo.

The fact that immature swifts have been caught in June as far south as the Sudan indicates that not all fly to Europe for the summer. Why do young swifts not remain in Africa and so avoid the hazardous journeys to and from Europe and Asia? Again one must accept that a behaviour pattern has evolved which determines that non-breeders as well as breeders should migrate, and that this has

survival value for the species. I shall return to this topic again.

A summer migrant which has until recently been assumed to breed exclusively in Europe is the swallow *Hirundo rustica*; but we now know that the same species breeds in South Africa. A single swallow ringed in Britain has been found dead beneath a nest in South Africa, but such circumstances, while compromising, fall short of proof that the same birds breed in Europe and Africa. It is certainly possible, though it would seem highly improbable; swallows raise two broods in Europe during the summer and it would be a prodigious effort to raise more immediately following their return to Africa. Perhaps a separate breeding population has become established in Africa which no longer makes the journey north.

Another curious and unexplained feature of swift migration is that the European species which breed furthest north in the summer migrate furthest south for the winter. The pallid swift nests on the northern shores of the Mediterranean and travels a mere 3200 kilometres (2000 miles) to the Sudan each winter;

Chris Mead, of the British Trust for Ornithology, had these swift nestboxes built into his new house. Alternatively they may be suspended under the eaves

the alpine swift travels further, 5600 kilometres (3500 miles) from Switzerland to Zaire; and the European swift furthest of all, 9700 to 11,300 kilometres (6000 to 7000 miles), from as far north as Lapland to South Africa. It is as though the migrations of each species were under the control of some cosmic pendulum, swinging north and south, spring and autumn.

When swifts do return to Europe each spring, it is to seek out human habitation. Before villages and towns were built of brick and stone swifts must have nested in holes in cliffs and other natural habitats, including trees, as some do even today. But for centuries swifts have sought out recesses under the roofs of old buildings or other structures as places in which to nest. Although human contact with swifts has been minimal we have in fact been accommodating swifts in our homes and buildings for a very long time. In this way we have probably helped the swift to increase in

numbers, since the availability of nest sites is an important factor in limiting bird populations.

As old buildings in which swifts have nested for years are demolished new sites become progressively harder to find. Modern buildings do not allow birds access into roof spaces, and in our present energy-conscious society we seal and insulate the roofs of those older buildings which are being preserved.

In the summer of 1978 a team of observers carried out a most painstaking and thorough survey of swift populations in the county of Northamptonshire (*Northamptonshire Bird Report*, 1979). An analysis of the types of buildings occupied by swifts showed that two-storey Victorian houses were most highly favoured as they allowed easy access into roof spaces, with room for the colonies to expand where the houses were built in terraces. Significantly, and perhaps ominously for future generations of swifts, not a single building erected since 1965 was occupied. It will be interesting to see if the disappearance of traditional nest sites has any long-term effect on the swift population, or indeed on the numbers of house sparrows and starlings which also seek out crannies and recesses in buildings for their nests.

Fortunately, swifts take readily to nest-boxes, and the installation of properly constructed boxes under the eaves would help compensate for the loss of nesting sites as well as provide an opportunity to study the birds at close quarters. In a few localities in Britain where nest-boxes have been installed and the occupants studied, the nesting swifts have been a source of absorbing interest.

In his book *The Birdman*, Major Henry Douglas-Home, who thinks the swift the most fascinating of all the birds he has come across, tells how in 1953 he installed ten nest-boxes, of his own design, under the window-sills of his home, The Hirsel, in the Scottish Border country. Since 1954 all the boxes have been occupied, some by the same pairs returning there year after year. He relates how he once took HRH Prince Philip to see his swifts, when his brother Alec, then Prime Minister, was in conference with HM The Queen at The Hirsel. Prince Philip was so excited by what he saw that he straight away ordered twenty-five nest-boxes, to be installed on the terraces at Windsor Castle ready for the swifts arriving the following spring.

Were it not that swifts – unapproachable when on the wing and untraceable somewhere in Africa for two-thirds of the year – take readily to nest-boxes and tolerate being watched at very close range, we should know very little of their life.

The best-known colony of swifts occupy the nest-boxes installed in the Oxford Tower by Dr Lack. For more than thirty years these birds have given immeasurable pleasure to a privileged few, amateur bird-watchers as well as professional ornithologists, who have visited the Tower during the breeding season and experienced that special kind of excitement that comes from observing completely wild creatures behaving normally at very close range.

Even for the few, with the notable exception of David and Elizabeth Lack, visits to the Tower must necessarily be short and infrequent. To enjoy the swifts fully one should watch them for several hours each day throughout at least one breeding season, and this I was fortunate to be able to do while making my documentary film, beginning in the spring of 1976 and continuing until the end of the breeding season of 1977.

The summer of 1976, it will be recalled, was the hottest and driest in Britain within living memory. In fact there had not been weather like it since 1726, and so by an extraordinary coincidence, and as it turned out by great good fortune, 1976 was uniquely different, for the birds as for us. Their special adaptations to survive conditions of cold and wet, so characteristic of the English summer, were not called upon and, on the contrary, the young birds suffered horribly in the heat. But the summer of 1977 once again followed the normal pattern, so the two years provided an insight into the way of life of the swifts, both in a normal year and in one so exceptional as to occur only once in more than two centuries.

A party of screamers flashes past the Tower; the nestboxes are behind the cone-shaped flutes

3

Swifts usually arrive in England at the end of April or the beginning of May, although if spring is cold and late their arrival may be delayed for one or two weeks. Swallows and martins reach England a little earlier. To the casual observer swallows, martins and swifts all look similar on the wing, but they are in fact quite distinctively different. The swallow, house martin and sand martin are classified together in the same family of the Order *Passeriformes,* whereas the swift belongs to a separate Order, the *Apodiformes,* the 'legless ones'.

Swallows, the traditional harbingers of summer, have pointed wings of gun-metal blue, a deeply forked tail, white breast and russet throat. They build a nest of mud, hay and feathers in recesses or attached to the walls of old buildings, or on beams and rafters in stables and barns. In the autumn they congregate in large numbers, usually on telephone wires, before migrating south for the winter; their departure signals the end of summer, as their arrival heralds its beginning.

The characteristic feature of the house martin *Delichon urbica* is its very distinctive white rump, which shows up particularly well in flight. House martins are gregarious birds and nest in colonies, attaching their cup-shaped nests of mud under the eaves of old buildings or the arches of bridges. Sand martins *Riparia riparia* also nest in colonies, burrowing deep into cliffs of sand on river banks or old quarries. They are smaller and less conspicuous than other members of the family, their plumage being a uniform brown, with pale throat and underparts, and a brown band across the breast.

There is no mistaking either the sight or sound of the swift. No other bird has the black profile, the long crescent-shaped wings or the

The Museum of Science, University of Oxford

The Swallow, *Hirundo rustica*, nests in old buildings, attaching its bracket nest of mud and straw, lined with feathers, to a beam or wall

speed of the swift, and its scream is quite different from the conversational twitter of the swallow or the martins.

In 1976 the first swifts arrived in Oxford on 1 May. In the old university city, spring is welcomed with traditional May Day festivities; a choir sings from the tower of Magdalen College soon after sunrise and Morris men perform their ancient dances in the streets as did their forebears centuries ago. As the sound of music and dancing rose above the turrets and pinnacles on that bright May morning, from a clear blue sky came the screams of swifts, performing dances even more ancient than those of the Morris men.

Since they had left Oxford the previous August the swifts had been flying continuously, night and day, month after month, until the time had come for their return. One in six of those that had embarked on the outward journey would have died somewhere between Oxford and southern Africa. Estimates of the mortality rate of both European and alpine swifts in different parts of Europe, based on ringing records, agree that about one-sixth of the adult swifts die each year, a lower death-rate than for any other wild bird so far studied in Europe or North America.

Some of the swifts would be returning to Oxford for the first time, but others would have

The House martin; *Delichon urbica* lives in colonies and builds its mud nest under the eaves

Sand martins, *Riparia riparia*, are also colonial and nest in burrows excavated in quarries or river banks

made the journey year after year. Meeting again each spring are birds which, though related, or mates of earlier years, would not have seen one another in the nine months since they last left Oxford.

For some of the swifts that wheeled and screamed in the crisp air over Oxford on May Day the end of their long journey from southern Africa was the Tower of the University Museum.

The University Museum of Science was built in the middle of the last century with money provided by the sale of Bibles. But the harmony between Church and Science which existed when the foundation stone was laid in 1855 had changed to discord by the time the building was finished. The theory of evolution

Left: A Swift's view of the Tower; the end of a journey of 6,000 miles from southern Africa

The interior of the Museum

by natural selection, proposed by Darwin and Wallace, shattered the long-established belief that all living things had been created separately as Acts of God; when Darwin's *The Origin of Species* (full title: *The Origin of Species by Means of Natural Selection or the Preservation of Favoured Races in the Struggle for Life*) was published in 1859 the controversy it aroused caused a rift between Church and Science which has since narrowed but is even now not closed. In 1860 the confrontation between faith and reason came to a head in the famous debate between the Bishop of Oxford, Samuel Wilberforce, and Thomas Henry Huxley, which took place in the University Museum. During the debate Wilberforce made the mistake of using ridicule instead of reasoned argument, questioning Huxley concerning his descent from an ape, a provocation welcome to Huxley, who replied with devastating effect that he would rather have an ape as an ancestor than a divine who used authority to stifle the truth.

The Museum is an architectural wonder, an extraordinary combination of brick and stone, wrought iron and glass, in a style perhaps best described as Victorian Gothic chateau. In the main exhibition hall columns of multi-coloured stones like tree trunks support girders with branches and leaves of wrought iron, reaching up to a glass sky. Among the fossils and the skeletons, the stuffed animals, and the collections of minerals and insects, scholars and schoolchildren gaze at birds in glass cases displaying in death their once glorious plumage, their bright eyes unseeing and deaf to the screams of the swifts that live in the Tower above.

Rising sixty feet above the vaulted glass roof of the Museum, the Tower dominates its surroundings. Access to the Tower is by a narrow stone spiral staircase; eighty steps lead to the first landing and from there ladders reach to platforms at four levels in the roof itself.

The swift nest-boxes are fitted into disused cone-shaped ventilation flutes. They open to the exterior in such a way that the entrance holes overhang the very steep slate roof, giving the birds a clear flight path in and out. Forty of

Inside the Tower a series of ladders reaches into the roof

Platforms at four levels allow access to the nestboxes installed behind the ventilation flutes

the boxes offer 'semi-detached' accommodation for two pairs of swifts, side by side but separated by a central partition. There are also sixty-seven single boxes at the lowest level in the Tower, so that 147 pairs of birds can be accommodated.

With so many nest-boxes accommodation is not a factor limiting the number of swifts living in the Tower, and it is thus possible to assess fluctuations in the population from other causes. Since boxes were first installed in 1948 the size of the colony has increased and now stands at thirty to forty breeding pairs.

In the first two weeks of May 1976 the most popular nest-boxes, those used year after year, mostly at the highest levels, were reoccupied, first by single birds and then by pairs, as mates of previous years were reunited or new partnerships formed.

The first to return explored the nest-boxes in a very tentative and uncertain manner, as though unsure of themselves. To birds that have enjoyed the infinite expanse and freedom of the skies for the previous nine months, and for those nesting for the first time at an age of three or even four years, the confines of a box so small that they have difficulty in turning round must seem very strange indeed. They were also very nervous and when disturbed, as for instance when the lid of the nest-box was raised, they would quickly shuffle to the entrance hole and drop out.

These were anxious days for us too. For months, during the winter, I had been making

Right: A swift leaves its nest in one of the flutes

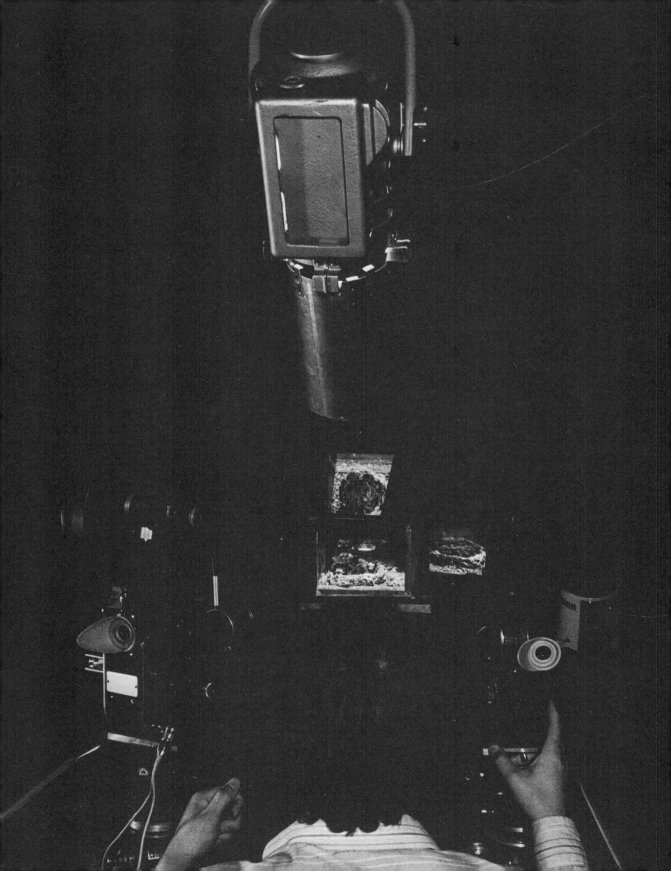

preparations for filming the swifts in the Tower during the summer, with my colleague Tony Allen, a university photographer. We had modified nest-boxes to permit filming from a distance of only a few inches, and installed powerful lights.

All our plans and preparations would come to nothing if the birds could not tolerate our interference; and not merely tolerate, but completely disregard our activities so that they would behave perfectly normally in front of the camera. In *Swifts in a Tower* David Lack describes how nesting birds were not disturbed by the light of a torch shone on them for brief periods, but we would be asking them to ignore a 750 watt spotlamp pouring an intense light on them from only two feet away, and for hours at a time.

The first trial only increased our apprehension. Choosing a pair of birds that had overcome their initial nervousness and seemed well established, though not yet nest-building, we brought a lamp to bear on the open nest-box and gradually increased the level of light. This was at 10.30 p.m.; it was quite dark outside, and we reasoned that the birds would be somewhat reluctant to leave the nest-box at night and more inclined to accept the light inside. Not at all; to our dismay the birds became frightened as soon as there was enough light to see by, left the nest-box in panic and did not return again that night.

Fortunately, we found that some other pairs of birds were very tolerant, and it became clear that swifts differ in their reactions to human interference and also in their general behaviour, to the extent that as time went by we attributed distinct personalities to them.

The two pairs eventually selected as our film stars were in adjoining nest-boxes at the highest level in the Tower, facing south. They had responded well to the initial tests, and within a week, during which time the intensity of the lights shining into the boxes had progressively been increased, we were able to watch them in the full glare of the spotlamps.

At full power the light from a 750 watt lamp is intense and would certainly damage the human eye if looked at directly for a few seconds, yet the swifts were apparently quite unaffected, even after hours of exposure to the light, with their eyes fully open. Nor were their eyes shielded by a nictitating membrane. Such a membrane, which can be drawn across the eyeball, is believed to afford protection from the glare of the sun for such high-flying birds as eagles and vultures, but these birds look down to find their food whereas the swift, flying for most of its life nearer the sun than any other bird, must be able to take a tiny insect out of the air with great precision and from any angle, even with the sun in its eyes. Perhaps the fact that the swifts in the Tower were unaffected by the intense brightness of the spotlamps is evidence of one more special adaptation to their aerial way of life.

Watching the birds bathed in light and quite unconcerned, we found it hard to believe that their instincts lead them to choose dark recesses under roofs as nest sites. Evidently, once our swifts had established themselves in darkened nest-boxes the fact that they were subsequently illuminated was unimportant, so long as they were unmolested and could not see into the Tower itself. Swifts have poor night vision; birds returning late to their nests have been seen to fly off after failing in several attempts to locate the nest entrance in poor light. When the interior of the Tower was in darkness and the nest-box brightly lit the birds could see nothing beyond the pool of light, and we could sit in silence and watch, only inches away but invisible in the darkness.

Since most of the action in the nest-boxes takes place in the early morning, we made a routine of arriving at the Tower soon after dawn each day and watching the birds until the sun had warmed up the air outside and they had left to feed. We came back at intervals during the day and then again in the evening to see them come in for the last time and settle down for the night. In this way we hoped to watch, and of course record on film, all the various aspects of swift behaviour that had been described by other observers and, with luck, some that had not.

We could sit in darkness with our cameras and watch the swifts without disturbing them

4

We could see that our two pairs of birds had rings on their legs, but we dared not catch them to read the numbers on the rings, and so find out about their previous histories, because handling the birds would very likely have caused them to desert. Swifts usually mate with the same partners as in the previous year, although over a period of several years an individual may change its partner and even return to its original mate after an interlude.

Several species of birds mate for life, notably swans, geese and crows among our common birds, but these are species which can stay together the year round. Swifts travel immense distances and are constantly on the wing. There is no reason to believe that pairs stay together outside the breeding season, since there is no biological advantage to be gained from remaining in contact. So each spring the birds must meet again, to renew the bonds forged in the previous year, and their rendezvous is the place where they last nested.

On the wing, courtship takes the form of high-speed chases and virtuoso aerobatics to the accompaniment of high-pitched screams. In the privacy of the nest-box it is a much more intimate affair, involving protracted mutual grooming. The two birds sit side by side and for several minutes at a time they take turns to preen one another, running their small beaks through the feathers of the head and throat. In between sessions they doze together, their heads touching, until one will suddenly awake and begin grooming the other. A very characteristic component of the grooming pattern is for one of the pair to offer its vulnerable throat to its mate by pointing its beak in the air and allowing its partner to run its beak up the throat, from breast to head. We were to see this behaviour from the time the pairs first came

A pair at rest after months, or even years, on the wing. Both sexes look alike

together in the nest-box and the impression they gave was one of mutual pleasure and affection.

It may be supposed that for a bird that spends its life on the wing, and thus cannot preen itself as do other birds, mutual grooming would serve a functional, as well as a ritual purpose, for example in removing parasites from the head and throat. The swift is host to many parasitic feather mites and lice, which can be seen running through the feathers of the head and particularly around the eyes and nostrils. But neither partner makes any attempt to pick them off its mate, and the grooming appears to be entirely directed towards establishing and strengthening the pair bonds.

The two sexes look so much alike that it is impossible to tell which is which unless their behaviour is unequivocally male or female, as when mating. It was during the course of one of the grooming sessions that we first saw mating take place in the nest. In the early morning of 26 May the two birds were sitting alongside one another, close together in the nest. At about 8.30 a.m., after several minutes of mutual grooming, the male twisted sideways and clutched the female by the feathers of her back with his small sharp claws. She twisted her body to meet his and the act of copulation took place, lasting a few seconds. Still maintaining his grip, the male rested for about twenty seconds, and the act was repeated. The two birds then separated, and the female preened the feathers on her back where they had been ruffled. Mutual grooming was resumed, and shortly afterwards the two birds left the box for the day.

Experienced observers have reported seeing swifts mating on the wing, but this must be a rare event. In our two summers of fairly concentrated surveillance we saw swifts come together in the air on only three occasions. The first was at the Tower in the spring, when two birds, already locked together near one of the flutes when we first saw them, fluttered downwards for a few feet before separating and flying away. As mating on the wing takes place in the open sky away from buildings and other obstructions, this encounter was probably

Swifts mate in the nest, usually in the morning; one of the few occasions when the sexes can be distinguished

A swift taking a feather from the air for its nest (both pictures are stills from the film *Devil Birds*)

40

either the end of a fight started in the nest-box or an accidental collision of two birds flying close to the flutes. On the other two occasions the behaviour of the two pairs of swifts exactly fitted the accounts given of aerial mating: one bird, presumably the male, approached the female from above and behind; the two were locked together in a long fluttering glide for several seconds; and then they separated. The first of these encounters was in May, during the mating season, but the second took place on 16 July 1977, long after egg-laying had ceased. The English naturalist A. S. Cutcliffe, whose observations over many years of a colony of swifts living in a tower in Ilfracombe, Devon, have made an important contribution to our knowledge of the swift, is unconvinced that successful coition takes place in flight. He too records observations of what he calls simulated coition at dates later than the period when eggs are laid, as late as 4 August in 1954. Perhaps these acts of 'simulated coition' late in the season have meaning as a ritual, a reinforcement of the pair bond, and are not for the purpose of producing fertile eggs. Swans copulate outside the breeding season and this has been explained as a means of strengthening or maintaining the bond between the pair.

It would help to arrive at a correct interpretation of the swifts' behaviour if one could see what was happening when the two birds are locked together, but the action is over in a few seconds and takes place high in the sky and at a speed that is hard to follow by eye, so it is likely that the swift's intimate secret will remain so for a very long time.

Nest-building is a very casual affair, as the swift has no need for an elaborate nest; a simple shallow bowl is sufficient. What remains of last year's nest is rehabilitated by cementing new materials to the rim with saliva. Nest materials are very varied – feathers, bits of paper, bus tickets, hay, seeds – anything taken on the wing. In 1976 elm seeds formed a major component of the nests in the Tower, the release of winged seeds from several large elms lining the road between the Tower and Keble College opposite coming at just the right time for the swifts. But by 1977 Dutch elm disease had taken its toll of these trees, as it has of millions of others throughout the country, and they are no longer there to provide the swifts with seeds for their nests.

By the time the swifts arrive in the spring the nest-boxes they abandoned in a very unsavoury condition the previous autumn have largely been cleansed by the action of bacteria and microfauna, and the materials making up the nests themselves have deteriorated during the winter as they have decomposed or been eaten by feather-eating mites and moth caterpillars. Although the adults take care not to foul the nest-box the chicks have no other recourse than to defaecate over the rim of the nest, and during the summer faecal pellets accumulate all around. The young of passerine birds produce pellets in a form which is taken immediately by an adult and disposed of some distance away, so that the nest does not become fouled and predators are given no clue to the whereabouts of the chicks. Swifts nest in places inaccessible to predators and the removal of faecal pellets is unnecessary.

In the debris of last year's nest are shiny black pupae of the louse-fly *Crataerina*

In the dust and debris of last year's nest, passively waiting for the return of the swifts in the spring and looking like so many shiny, black vitamin pills, are the pupae of the blood-sucking louse-fly *Crataerina pallida*. The swift

After lying dormant all winter the pupae resume their development in the spring, as temperatures rise

which there is no escape, should be a parasitic fly, only one-third of an inch long, which has lost the power of flight. *Crataerina* spends almost its entire life in the immediate vicinity of the nest, its only excursions outside as a passenger among the swift's feathers. Wings would serve it no useful function, either in the nest site or when clinging to its host, and they have become vestigial. But a powerful grip is all-important and the feet of *Crataerina* are highly specialized for gripping feathers. Each foot is equipped with a combination of claws and suction pads which enable the fly to run quickly forwards or sideways and yet grip feathers very firmly.

Towards the end of summer the female *Crataerina* produces larvae, one at a time, which have developed from eggs fertilized inside her body, and these larvae are deposited in the nest debris where they immediately pupate. The adult fly dies, but the pupae lie dormant all winter. In badly infested nests thirty or forty pupae are not uncommon. Their further development in the spring is timed to coincide with the return of the swifts, the pupae hatching at about the time that the first eggs are laid.

has few enemies, its speed and agility on the wing being such that it falls prey only rarely, and probably then only when weakened, to a hobby or other bird of prey. It is one of Nature's ironies that the swift's greatest enemy, from

43

5

One morning, in the last week of May, we were making our routine inspections of the nests in the Tower when, on opening the lid of one of the boxes, we found a single pure white egg; and sitting on the egg a newly hatched louse-fly, attracted by its warmth.

In the next few days eggs appeared in all the nests occupied by breeding pairs, until each contained a full clutch of two or three. We were able to observe and film our two females laying their eggs, which they did in the mornings, between 7.30 a.m. and 10.00 a.m.

Each female behaved quite differently. The first appeared to find the act of laying very difficult. Rising from the nest as high as her very short legs would allow she extended her body and expelled the egg by a series of contractions which clearly involved great effort. The second female laid her eggs with such ease that we were only sure of what had happened on each occasion after she had left the nest and the egg was there to be seen. Instead of stretching forward she hunched her body and drooped her wings, tucking her head down between her legs, seemingly to help the egg out with her beak. Once, when her mate was present during egg-laying, he appeared to be very interested, and both indulged in a session of mutual grooming when the egg had been laid, as though congratulating one another on their achievement.

The difference in behaviour between the two females may well have been because the first was young, possibly laying for the first time, while the second bird was older and had produced eggs in previous seasons. A swift's egg weighs about $3\frac{1}{2}$ grams (about one-eighth of an ounce), which is one-twelfth the weight of the bird, and for a young inexperienced female it must be a great strain to lay an egg of such a size.

Two or three white eggs are laid at the end of May or early June

Swifts lay a clutch of two or three eggs, which are pure white, as are those of other birds nesting in holes, where pigmentation is irrelevant; indeed, white eggs are more easily seen in the darkness. Clutch size in birds is related to the number of young which can be reared successfully to adulthood. For the swift, which has few natural predators and whose chicks are virtually immune from attack, except perhaps by an occasional marauding rat in a roof, the

limit on clutch size is imposed by food supply, and thus weather. Two or three chicks are as many as can be fed in a normal summer, and when the weather is poor one or more of these may starve to death.

Many observers have reported finding eggs, and occasionally the entire clutch, outside the nest and apparently abandoned, and this has been explained as the swift's way of reducing the size of its clutch if bad weather follows egg-laying. Eggs outside the nest are abandoned, in that the birds make no attempt to recover them. There are reports of eggs being found so far from the nest that they could not have rolled there by accident, but whether eggs are deliberately ejected from the nest to reduce clutch size in bad weather is open to question. Such a supposition would imply a prescience of poor weather conditions at the time when the

Left: The louse-fly *Crataerina* hatches at about the time the first eggs are laid

Below: We could replace eggs found outside the nest without disturbing the sitting birds

chicks would have hatched and needed feeding, and not when the eggs were being incubated.

The weather in June 1976 was consistently fine and hot. At no time was there a shortage of food, and yet about as many eggs were found outside the nests as in a normal year. To find out if eggs had deliberately been ejected, if not because of the weather then possibly because they were infertile, we replaced some of the abandoned eggs in the nests. All of these eggs were accepted and later hatched, suggesting that they had not actively been expelled, nor were they infertile.

An explanation more consistent with the facts is that eggs are rolled out of the nest by accident, and once beyond the rim are abandoned. Both parent swifts share the incubation of the eggs, and at the change-over they first greet one another by ritual grooming, and then the in-coming bird takes the place of its mate on the eggs. Quite often this is more of a displacement, achieved in spite of a determined resistance from its mate against being turned out of the nest. At such times the change-over is very disorderly, exacerbated in the confined space of the nest-box by the birds' absurdly short legs and very long wings. As the nest itself is no more than a shallow bowl it is easy for an egg to be rolled over the rim, and when one sees how awkwardly the birds move about in the nest-box it is not surprising that eggs are lost accidentally in this way. This explanation does not exclude the possibility of *some* eggs being deliberately ejected, as for instance when an egg is chipped or cracked or when the bird senses that it is infertile.

Although the first egg laid is not incubated during the day-time, one of the pair sits on it in the nest at night. This early start to incubation results in the first egg hatching before the others, by one or two days. Full-time incubation begins when the second egg is laid, and if

With long, narrow wings shaped for speed, and short weak legs, a swift that is brought down has a poor chance of survival

there is a third egg, after another day or two, this hatches last of all. As a result, a brood of newly hatched chicks in their first week of life are of different sizes; if there is a shortage of airborne insects at this time the largest and strongest of the chicks obtains a greater share of the available food. Should food continue to be scarce the weaker siblings may even starve to death but at least one chick should survive, unless conditions become extreme.

A similar adaptation to an uncertain food supply is found among other birds, in particular birds of prey, but the swift is the only insectivorous species known to stagger hatching in this way. Why do other migratory birds, such as swallows and martins, apparently very like swifts in behaviour and diet, lay a larger clutch of eggs, usually five, which hatch together? The answer must lie in the unique ecological niche occupied by the swift. Swifts are essentially and supremely birds of the open skies. Their speed and endurance enables them to comb vast areas of space for air-borne insects, the aerial plankton, carried high by the wind. The nearer they come to the ground the more vulnerable they are to being brought down accidentally, and a downed swift is doomed. Among the trees and hedgerows insects are much more abundant, but there speed is less important than manoeuvrability; this niche is occupied by the swallows, martins, flycatchers and others, all of which can land and take off again. Swifts fly low in bad weather, but when they do they prefer water or other open localities free of obstacles, where they can fly at speed and with safety. So the swift is, paradoxically, restricted to open spaces, where its food supply is scarcer and far more uncertain, being so much more under the influence of the weather, than lower down in fields and among trees.

Swifts incubate their eggs for nineteen days, nearly a week longer than for song-birds of a similar size. As it sits for hours at a time the bird whose turn it is to incubate occupies itself in a manner which in humans would be interpreted as an expression of boredom – dozing, preening, fidgeting, yawning and perfunctory nest-building. For most of the time the bird sits facing away from the nest entrance and into the darkness. Although the birds we were filming sat in a pool of bright light they behaved no differently from those in darkness. After peering up at the light when it was first switched on they completely ignored it.

The evident tedium of sitting on the eggs is aggravated by the irritations of parasites. In common with all birds swifts are host to several different kinds of parasitic feather lice (*Mallophaga*) and mites. Two genera of feather-lice, *Dennyus* and *Eureum*, are peculiar to swifts; another group, the *Ischocera*, are never found on swifts although they parasitize all other birds.

As the swifts in the Tower incubate their eggs, mites emerge from the feathers around the head and make their way to the nostrils, into which they disappear. Occasionally a feather-louse sidles into view but it usually vanishes again immediately unless it emerges on the head, when it may crawl to the corner of the eye and commence feeding. The louse appears to be taking in the fluid bathing the eye-ball, presumably because of its nutritive value, and this evidently irritates the swift, which shakes its head and scratches with its foot.

Mites and feather-lice, though they may irritate, are very small and presumably do the swift no appreciable harm. The louse-fly *Crataerina*, on the other hand, is relatively enormous and a serious pest of adult swifts and nestlings. Louse-flies, or flat-flies as they are sometimes called, of the genus *Crataerina* parasitize house martins, and to a lesser extent swallows, as well as swifts, but not sand martins; presumably the latter's tunnels, damp and liable to collapse, are an unsuitable habitat for the *Crataerina* pupae to survive the winter.

The unfortunate house martin has the distinction of being one of the most heavily parasitized of all birds, its mud nest providing a habitat in which many ectoparasites live and breed, and survive the winter. In the spring, when the house martins return to refurbish their nests they are assailed by fleas, mites and lice as well as by large numbers of louse-flies (*Crataerina hirundinis*). Populations of over

A feather-louse feeds in the corner of a swift's eye as it sits incubating its eggs

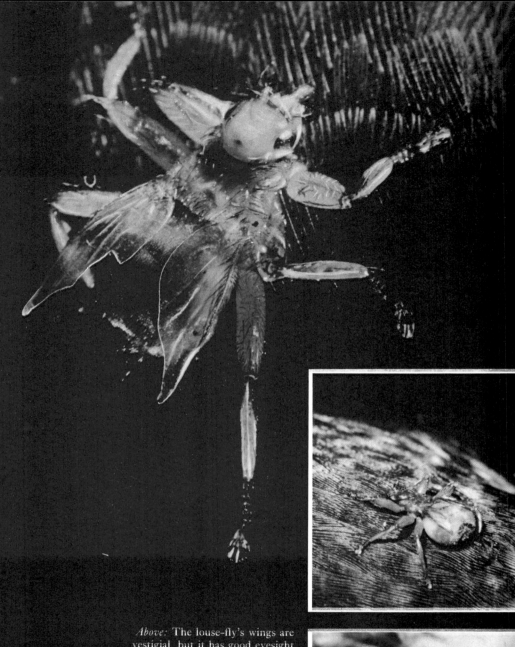

Above: The louse-fly's wings are vestigial, but it has good eyesight and feet specialized for gripping feathers

Above right: Until the chicks hatch *Crataerina* feeds on the adult swift

Right: The chicks passively provide meals of blood from the time they hatch

Below: A newly hatched louse-fly; within minutes it will harden and be ready for a meal of blood

Right: The head of a louse-fly; blood is sucked through a fine tube sheathed in a hairy proboscis

Above: A newly laid larva of a louse-fly; it will pupate almost immediately

Right: A louse-fly's foot is equipped with special hooks and pads for gripping feathers

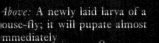

100 louse-flies have been recorded in the nests of house martins, which is a higher density than is usual for swifts parasitized by *Crataerina pallida*.

In the Tower a count of thirty to forty pupae per nest is not uncommon. When the fly hatches in late May or early June, the puparium cap at the head end of the insect is forced off and the fly emerges, pale, soft-limbed and with shrivelled wings. Within a few minutes the colour darkens as the skin hardens, the legs stiffen and the vestigial wings expand. *Crataerina* is then ready to take a meal of blood from the adult swift, which it does about once every five days, sucking in some 25 milligrams of blood each time through its retractable proboscis. For heavily infested swifts the blood loss must be appreciable, and birds already weak may well succumb. There are reports of swifts found dying on the ground carrying twenty or more louse-flies, and these would, of course, also be doomed with the death of their hosts.

The swifts in the Tower were certainly irritated by the attentions of *Crataerina*, preening whenever they felt the fly's proboscis. However, the birds always closed their eyes when preening and *Crataerina* merely had to sidle out of the way of the bird's beak to avoid being damaged. It is surprising that a swift, which can seize a tiny insect out of the air at full speed, is apparently unable to rid itself of a large fly actually sucking its blood. There are reports of house martins attempting to remove *Crataerina* but the louse-fly is extremely tough and grips feathers so tightly that the bird would be unlikely to damage the fly. In common with other ectoparasites, such as fleas and lice, *Crataerina* is not harmed by treatment which normally kills other insects. Attempting to crush a louse-fly between finger and thumb, as we did at first when finding them in our clothes after sessions in the Tower, was totally ineffective as the fly was able to run away quite unharmed once it had been released. Its grip on feathers is quite extraordinary. To test how powerful a hold it has I once held a louse-fly by forceps and induced it to grip the feathers on the back of a recently dead swift which we had found in the Tower. Trying to break the fly's hold by lifting it off the feathers with the forceps I was able to raise the entire body of the swift into the air, so strong was the *Crataerina*'s grip.

The sight of several louse-flies running over a swift, with extraordinary speed, and burrowing under its feathers to suck blood, arouses a strong feeling of revulsion. There is something obscene about louse-flies which may touch a primitive chord in our own make-up. One cannot help putting oneself in the place of the swift and imagining how it would feel to have 10-centimetre (4-inch) long parasites, the size of shore-crabs, scuttling in and out of one's clothing, each taking about a quarter of a pint of blood every five days.

To be realistic, a healthy swift can survive the attentions of *Crataerina* with no apparent illeffect, and only in a few instances have heavily infested swifts been found dying in a manner which suggested that they had been weakened by loss of blood. The life of a parasite is normally so well adapted to that of its host that it is unusual for the latter to be killed; if this does happen the parasite usually dies too.

What had started as a heatwave in May 1976, before the eggs were even laid, extended into a long period of consistent sunshine and high temperatures. By 7 June, thermometers in the nest-boxes were recording temperatures exceeding 30° C (86° F) and as the sun continued to gain strength during the month temperatures in the Tower rose above 38° C (100° F) by mid afternoon. The sitting birds kept as cool as possible by panting with open beaks, losing heat by evaporation from the lining of the throat. At such times one can see that although the swift has a very small beak it has an enormous gape, in common with other birds that catch insects on the wing, in particular the nightjars, and notably the Australian frogmouth. The full extent of the gape can only be seen when the swift yawns, which it does not infrequently during incubation.

As well as panting and yawning the swifts occasionally vibrated head and beak very rapidly, for no more than two or three seconds at a time. Such behaviour, which occurs during the course of preening sessions in the nest, has not previously been reported. The vibration was so rapid, and was over so quickly, that it was difficult to be sure it had actually happened; in fact we were uncertain ourselves until we closely examined the film recording the event. What at first appeared to be a blurred and out-of-focus sequence of the swift's head proved, on analysis of the film, frame by frame, that the bird was in fact vibrating its beak and head at such a speed that the image on the film appeared as a blur. We later found that a photograph taken at 1/1000 second exposure was still too slow to freeze the movement of the head.

In preening, a swift sometimes vibrates its head so fast that it is blurred even when photographed with electronic flash at 1/1000 sec.

An explanation of such curious behaviour can only be tentative. It could be to dislodge parasites on the head, and perhaps in the nostrils, where mites congregate, but if so it has no effect that one can observe. More likely, in my view, is that it is a means by which the swift preens that part of its body which it cannot reach at all with its beak, and only very awkwardly and inefficiently with its claws. By vibrating the head at high speed, individual feathers separate, small particles of dirt and debris are shaken off and the feathers fit neatly into place again when the vibration ceases. A swift has special problems in preening, different from other birds. Being continuously on the wing it cannot rest to groom itself; its legs are so short that only with great difficulty can it scratch its head when in the nest, a difficulty presumably compounded when it is actually flying. One might suppose also that swifts have a particular need to groom the feathers of the head. They catch several thousand insects each day, many of which are soft-bodied and easily damaged on impact with a swift travelling at high speed; it is to be expected that insect juices and small fragments, as well as the swift's own saliva, will adhere to the feathers around the beak and head. Indeed this can be seen when swifts which are feeding chicks bring back food in their throat pouches. It is possible that while on the wing the swift cleanses and grooms the feathers of its head by vibrating them at high speed, in a manner similar to the way we use ultra-sonic vibration to clean clothing. What we observed as a rare event in the nest-box may normally occur while the bird is in flight.

In good weather only one bird at a time occupies the nest-box during the day, but each evening the partner last out returns to its mate sitting on the eggs and they spend the night together, sleeping side by side. They give every appearance of sleeping profoundly, and the fact that they benefit from a good night's sleep increases the mystery of how swifts rest when they are not nesting, and spend night after night on the wing.

Each evening at the Tower as the sun sets and the breeding pairs settle down for the night, groups of birds circle the Tower, screaming from time to time and rising higher as the sky grows darker, to disappear completely as night closes in.

We know now that these swifts are the immature non-breeders, joined occasionally by mature birds spending the night away from the nest. Speculation that swifts fly all night and sleep on the wing persisted for many years before being accepted as fact. It is illustrative of the perversity of human nature that the improbable legend of swallows hibernating in lakes was believed for centuries, whereas reports from responsible witnesses of swifts spending all night on the wing, backed by considerable circumstantial evidence, were treated with scepticism and even disdain, perhaps because it is hard to believe that a small bird can fly continuously night and day and actually sleep on the wing.

As long ago as the First World War a French airman reported an encounter with a flock of swifts at night. He had climbed to 4400 metres (14,500 feet) before cutting his engine and gliding silently down over the German lines. At about 3000 metres (10,000 feet) he saw below him, showing up clearly against the white clouds in the light of a full moon, a scattered group of birds which appeared to be drifting above the clouds and showed no reaction to the presence of the plane. As he flew through the flock one of the birds was accidentally trapped in the fuselage, and it turned out to be a swift. Convincing evidence, one might suppose, and there were other reports too, of swifts being heard and seen on the wing at night, yet in 1952 a correspondent of *The Times*, in an article dated 22 July and entitled 'Spying on Swifts', was asking sceptically 'Does the bird sometimes sleep on the wing, or at least spend the night flying, as some naturalists believe? That great authority, the *Handbook of British Birds*, says it is improbable. . . .'

By coincidence, in that same month David Lack saw for the first time a party of swifts, which had been feeding over the marshes along the Sussex coast, fly out to sea at dusk. He assumed then that they were returning to the Continent but in later years more detailed observations suggested that swifts which were either feeding along the coast or were in passage, responding to a major weather movement, regularly flew out to sea each evening, whatever the weather, to spend the night on the wing. It was not until *Swifts in a Tower* had gone to press that David Lack was able to confirm, in a postscript, that swifts in passage sleep on the wing, from having observed mass ascents of birds feeding over reservoirs, the swifts rising to a height of 100 or 200 feet before drifting away together.

A. S. Cutcliffe, in a contribution published in *British Birds* in 1955, describes how he saw and heard swifts flying well after dark on two occasions, on one of which he saw them flying through the searchlight beams of a warship lying at anchor.

In recent years the circumstantial evidence and eye-witness reports of swifts sleeping on the wing have been confirmed by studies in which sophisticated radar equipment has tracked large numbers of swifts as well as individual birds. Radar has proved very useful in bird studies, enabling migrant species and foraging birds, such as starlings, to be tracked over large areas. One of these studies, conducted by the Marconi Company, recorded on film a radar screen monitoring the sky over the London area and southern England, including the Channel. As the sun set and darkness fell all detail on the screen was blotted out as thousands upon thousands of swifts rose into the night sky, in what has come to be known as their Vespers flight.

In Switzerland swifts have been tracked by radar automatically, day and night. We now know that they spend the night high in the air in bad weather as well as fine, and when flying at night a swift alternates a phase of wing beats with one of rest. The beating phase is of 1 to 6 seconds duration, with wing-beat frequencies of 6 to 8 per second, while the resting phase lasts from 0.5 to 5 seconds. Non-migrating individuals fly at an air speed of about 23 k.p.h. (14 m.p.h.), while swifts migrating at night travel faster, at around 40 k.p.h. (25 m.p.h.). These studies have also confirmed eye-witness reports that the general pattern of migration of swifts is dominated by the passage of weather systems.

As far as is now known, the European swift is the only bird which ascends at night to sleep on the wing. For explanation we need look again at the unique way of life of a bird whose domain is the open sky. On the wing a swift is usually safe, but one that is brought down is in peril of its life. So unless some accident befalls it the swift

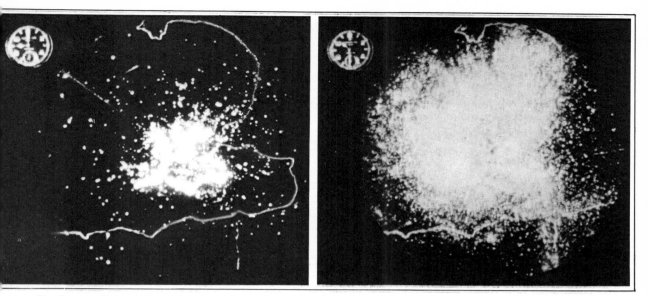

The Vespers flight of the swift over south-east England, as seen by radar
A photograph of the radar screen at 9.00 p.m. in mid-summer (June 22); the echoes of planes (large points of light) flying between the Wash, to the north, and the English Channel, show up clearly against the outline of the coast. At 10.30 p.m., as darkness falls, all detail on the screen is obliterated as thousands of swifts rise into the night sky to sleep on the wing (from film *Devil Birds*; *courtesy:* The Marconi Co. Ltd)

leaves its refuge in the sky only when it is essential to do so, as when nesting, and for the minimum period of time. Swifts do occasionally cling momentarily to the outside of a building in which there are nests, as if in play, usually towards the end of the breeding season but these are probably young birds that have recently left the nest.

Swifts are not only seasonally migratory, travelling thousands of miles each spring and autumn between Europe and Africa, but they also fly great distances during the summer in response to weather movements. Those that are rearing young usually restrict their foraging to within a hundred miles or so of their nest, but the non-breeders are free to range where they will and may fly up to a thousand kilometres in a single day to avoid a region of bad weather. Mass movements of swifts occur throughout the summer, the birds avoiding depressions and congregating in their thousands where there is abundant food. When these movements occur the swifts fly against the wind, thus avoiding the centre of the depression. Ranging the length and breadth of Europe they would not find safe roosting places every evening, in localities with which they were not familiar. So it is safer for them to remain in the air overnight, and by rising high above any tall buildings, trees or other obstacles, or when they are near a coastline by flying over the sea, they stay out of danger.

6

As one long, hot day followed another in May and June 1976, it became apparent that the summer was going to be quite exceptional. For the swifts, it meant an abundance of aerial plankton and there was no need for the birds to leave the eggs for long periods to search for food many miles away. In a normal year, if a spell of bad weather occurs while the eggs are being incubated, both parent birds make extended excursions to find food, and the eggs may be left for many hours and become chilled. The developing embryos inside the eggs do not die as would those of other birds in such circumstances; another of the swift's special adaptations to survive the adverse weather conditions to be expected in an average northern temperate summer.

In 1976, incubation of the eggs was continuous, and beginning in the third week of June, about nineteen days after they had been laid, the eggs hatched. The newly hatched chicks of our common passerine garden birds – robins, thrushes, blackbirds, hedgesparrows, tits, etc. – are unprepossessing, and bear little comparison with those of the nidifugous species, those that leave the nest as soon as they are dry after hatching, such as pheasants, plovers and waterfowl. But even among the passerines there can be few to compare with the young swift for ugliness. When newly hatched it is pink, naked and blind with a large stomach and enormous gape; as it grows and the down pushes through the skin, followed later by the emergence of the quills, it looks positively repulsive. But in nature it is survival not appearance that matters, and the young swift is marvellously adapted to grow fast and to survive conditions that would kill other birds.

All that is required of the young swift is that it should take in and digest large quantities of food, and for this it has an enormous gape and a large gut and liver. Its legs and feet are developed sufficiently to prop up the body when reaching for food; its brain and senses are little developed since it has no need for the alertness and coordination necessary to the survival of the young of nidifugous species. The most pronounced innate response is to react to a sudden sound by reaching up with open beak, since such a sound is usually caused by the arrival of a parent bird with food.

The nests we were filming in 1976 each contained three chicks, hatched a few days apart. The size difference was quite pronounced in the first few days, but within a week all had attained the same size because there was an abundance of insects, sufficient for all appetites. The most demanding chick was fed first and it was easy to see how, in a bad year, one would receive the lion's share of the available food, leaving the smaller and weaker siblings to go hungry and perhaps die.

It was astonishing to see how much the chicks could consume. The arrival of a parent is the signal for the chicks to reach up with beaks open and the adult, its pouch distended by a mass of insects stuck together with saliva, reaches as far as it can down the chick's throat to deliver a meal. When the chicks are very young the food bolus brought in by a parent is too big to ingest whole and it is shared among them. Even so, each portion seems enormous, almost as big as the chick's head. The meals appear so frequently in good weather, on average about once every hour from each parent alternately, that sometimes a chick will be so satiated that it falls asleep with the ball of insects still protruding from its beak.

From the day they hatch, and even, according to David Lack, while still in the shell, the young swifts call with a weak, piping cry, quite unlike the scream of the adult. When pleading

A day-old chick being fed; its meal of insects, part of the contents of the parent's pouch, can be seen as a dark mass passing down its throat

Above: Although the newly hatched chicks are blind, naked and helpless they are marvellously adapted to grow fast and survive conditions of cold and starvation that would kill other birds

Right: When insects are plentiful a very young chick may become so satiated that it falls asleep in the middle of a meal

for food this piping is much louder, and in the Tower we could tell when young were being fed by the sound of a swift entering a nest-box followed immediately by the excited piping of the chicks. Blind, and responding instinctively to a sudden sound, the chicks were often mistaken into thinking a parent had arrived by the rattling of slates in the wind, footsteps in the Tower, or even traffic noise outside. Occasionally when roused in this way, one of the chicks would try to swallow the head of a smaller brother or sister under the mistaken impression that it was a meal.

In the first week the naked chicks are brooded continuously, but during the second week they are left alone for much of the day while both parents are out catching sufficient food to satisfy their prodigious appetites. The chicks are not harmed by being left unbrooded, and

indeed, the young swift survives being chilled and going without food for long periods, circumstances which would quickly lead to the death of song-bird nestlings. Even a newly hatched swift can survive cold and starvation for several days. Until its feathers grow the young swift's temperature is about the same as that of its surroundings; only when it is brooded is it as warm as its parent. If left for several hours in cold weather the chicks may become chilled to the point of torpor, with stiffened limbs, but rally quickly when the parent bird returns with food. This is clearly a very important adaptation, similar to that of the embryo inside the egg, which can also survive being chilled.

In fact, helpless though it is, the young swift is better able to survive adverse conditions than its parents. A swift nestling can survive a fast of up to three weeks, under experimental conditions, if it is well grown and has had time to lay down layers of fat under the skin as an energy reserve, whereas the adult swift is very weak after starving for two or three days and usually dies after four days. This means that when there is a prolonged period of bad weather and insects are scarce the adult can at least feed itself, and thus survive until conditions improve, if necessary ranging so far from the nest that the young swift goes without food for days. Because the parents are not bound to the vicinity of the nest, the brood survives.

The young swift's ability to live on its reserves, and lose weight in adverse conditions, is matched by an equal facility for putting on weight when food is abundant. After a period of deprivation the nestlings can catch up very quickly, so that at the end of a single day's feeding they may actually have increased their weight by as much as a quarter of what it was in the morning.

In the summer of 1976 the chicks gorged themselves and one could almost see them grow by the hour. Within a few days the clean, bright pink skin of the newly hatched chick had

darkened and become blotchy as the down first appeared as blue-black streaks under the skin and then erupted into a grey fluff.

The louse-flies that had fed on the adult swift's blood transferred their attentions to the chicks as soon as they had hatched, without the chicks being either aware of or affected by their predations, as far as we could see. The flies made no more excursions with the adults and for the rest of the summer remained in the nest-box and fed on the young swifts.

By the second week of their lives the nestlings are able to swallow the entire food bolus brought in by the parent, instead of sharing it. An average meal weighs just over a gram (about one-thirtieth of an ounce) and the parents may each bring up to twenty meals on a good day, the highest recorded at the Tower being forty-two from one pair. The young swift converts insects into tissue and fat with an extraordinary efficiency, and within four weeks, in a good summer, it will have reached its maximum weight of 56 grams (2 ounces), from a

As each parent returns when its food pouch is full, the intervals between meals are determined by the availability of insects

weight at hatching of $2\frac{3}{4}$ grams (about one-tenth of an ounce), after which it loses weight as its feathers grow.

The parent swifts return with full food pouches whatever the weather, and the interval between meals is determined by the availability of insects. In good weather a swift may fill its pouch in less than an hour, or it may take several hours when food is scarce and consists mainly of small insects. As one would expect, swifts select the largest of those available to them on a particular day, providing they are not too large to fit into their pouch. Apart from selecting for size, and avoiding insects that sting, swifts are catholic in their tastes and take anything in the aerial plankton, from insects as minute as thrips to those as large as hoverflies. Each meal is composed of 300 to 500 individuals, and on a fine day a pair of swifts with young to feed may catch some 20,000 insects and spiders, representing hundreds of different species. No other bird is known which feeds on so many different food items, and in such numbers, as the swift.

An analysis of the diet of a bird, or any wild animal, is beset with difficulties. It is a subject on which data are in many cases inadequate or misleading, and for those animals which dare to compete with man, descriptions of their diet are often so clouded with prejudice as to be of doubtful value. Too often information on what an animal eats is obtained by a *post-mortem* analysis of the contents of its gut or gizzard. This procedure is unsatisfactory for the investigator, in that his examination is more often than not limited to the partly digested remains of a single meal, and is the ultimate misfortune for the animal which has to be sacrificed.

Fortunately for the swift, there is an easy and harmless method of finding out what it takes as food, providing there is access to the nest. If a young swift is taken immediately after it has been fed, the food bolus in its throat can be recovered by gentle manipulation with the

The arrival of the parent is a signal for the chicks to beg for food

In the summer of 1979 aphid populations reached 'plague' proportions; in places dense swarms rose like columns of smoke above the trees, where they were found by the swifts fingers. The bird is not harmed and merely goes without that particular meal. An adult can similarly be induced to eject the food bolus in its throat pouch before feeding its young, but there is some risk of it deserting if it is badly frightened and it is preferable to take a sample from the young bird.

The food ball is made up of a mass of insects stuck together with saliva, some of the insects still alive. Identification, even to families, of the hundreds of insects that make up each meal demands great patience and dedication by an experienced entomologist, but the results of such labours are very rewarding. Even a simple analysis shows the tremendous effect that swifts must have in reducing our insect populations during the summer, since each swift is capable of removing several thousand insects a day from the air and the population of swifts throughout Europe must run into millions.

One fact which analysis quickly brings to light is a great variation in the kinds and numbers of insects taken, even between samples collected on the same day. This reflects the differences in the abundance and behaviour of insects hour by hour and day by day, throughout the summer, according to their life cycles as well as the vagaries of the weather and such geographical factors as the proximity of lakes or reservoirs.

In the hot summer of 1976 hoverflies were particularly abundant, and their presence is typical of fine, warm days. Very common were dipterous flies and plant-bugs, including aphids, and the remainder comprised mainly of hymenopterans, beetles, and – curiously since they have no wings – a few spiders. It may seem surprising that spiders should be carried about in the aerial plankton hundreds of feet in the air, but spiders commonly travel by launching themselves into a breeze off some high point, trailing a silken thread as they go, and their bodies are so light that with the gossamer catching the air currents they can be whisked to great heights and transported for many miles. At certain times spiders, mostly belonging to the Family Linyphiidae, occur frequently in the samples; of fifty-eight meals taken from swifts in Oxford in 1952 and 1953, no less than fifty contained spiders.

There are years in which certain insects become so abundant that they assume plague proportions. In 1976 there were ladybirds everywhere, in huge numbers, festooning vegetation and even driving holiday-makers from the beaches. Yet relatively few ladybirds were present in the meals given to the chicks, and it was clear that the swifts were not taking them in the quantities one might expect. Ladybirds excrete a noxious fluid from their leg joints when threatened, and it may be for this reason that the swifts avoid them.

In 1979 it was the aphids whose population explosion in July reached plague proportions, with hardly a ladybird to be seen. Both the larva and the adult ladybird prey heavily on aphids and with ladybirds mysteriously scarce aphids multiplied in such numbers that on occasions they gave the appearance of columns of smoke rising vertically a hundred feet or so above the ground. Swifts found these concentrations and sliced into them in much the same way as tuna fish will attack a shoal of anchovies. Though they are small, aphids are highly nutritious, and in 1979 their abundance was reflected in the food brought to the young swifts in the Tower. One meal, collected in the first week of July, contained 726 aphids out of a total of 898 insects, the remainder comprising 48 leaf-hoppers, 23 crane-flies, 22 spittle-bugs, 18 dung-flies, 13 ladybirds, 10 ants, and small numbers of various flies, beetles, parasitic wasps, bugs and thrips.

It came as a surprise to find thrips among the insects caught by swifts because they are so minute, measuring less than a millimetre in length and scarcely visible to the human eye. One cannot help wondering how such a miniscule speck could possibly justify the energy used to catch it, quite apart from the miraculous vision required even to see it in the air when travelling at 40 to 50 k.p.h.

On 12 July two samples were collected at the same nest, one from each parent, as they arrived to feed their chicks within five minutes of one another. Not only were the compositions of

64

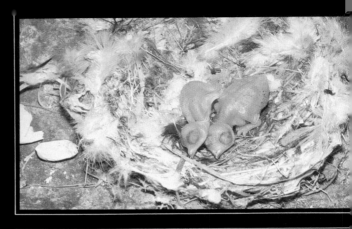

Right: Two chicks hatched on consecutive days; the shells of the eggs are leathery at the time of hatching, probably because the calcium in the shell has been utilized by the developing embryo

Above: The chicks are unaware of the presence of the louse-fly feeding on them, and apparently unaffected by it

Right: In good weather a chick will grow fast and after only six days may weigh over 20 gms, from a weight at hatching of 2¾ gms

Left: Feathers growing under the skin appear as blue streaks; they erupt first on the wings and tail

Left: These chicks in their second week have put on weight continuously and are beginning to sprout feathers

Left: When it yawns the young swift displays the full extent of its impressive gape

Above: A week-old chick being fed; to pass the food ball the parent reaches deep into its throat, closing its eyes for protection

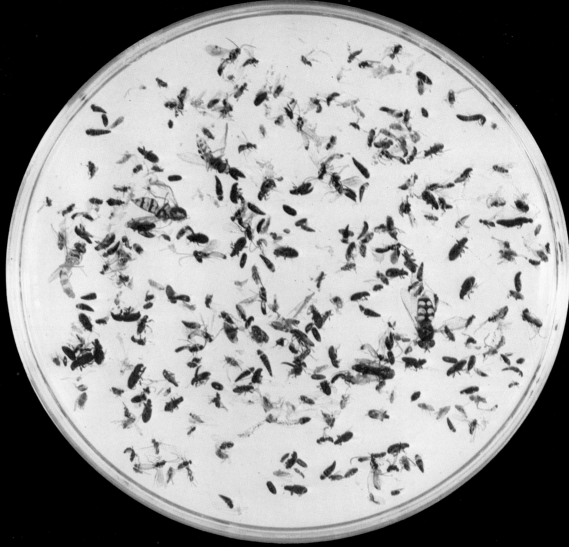

This food ball, recovered from a chick, contains several hundred insects stuck together with saliva; each meal weighs just over a gram

After insects have passed through a chick all that remains is undigestible chitin; the elytra of beetles may easily be identified, even to species

these two meals different from the sample above, taken a week earlier, but they were also different from each other. Aphids were present in hundreds in all these samples, but whereas in one of the pair the most common insects were leaf-hoppers (Delphacidae) of which there were 279 out of a total of 543, in the other the bulk of the meal was made up of hoverflies (Syrphidae), not represented at all in the first sample. The two parents were apparently hunting in different locations. Had we taken samples at different times during a single day we should also have seen evidence of how the composition of the meals varies from morning to evening. It is easy to see how the swift has adopted the habit of taking everything that flies or is carried in the aerial plankton, including spiders, except those which are too large, or which sting.

Analysis of the diet of swifts during the summer may explain why they normally migrate south at the end of the season some two months before the swallows and martins. Swifts begin to leave Oxford in the third week of July (about three months after their arrival) and most have gone by the third week in August. Exceptionally, late broods may not leave until the end of August or even into September, the latest departure ever recorded from the Tower being 21 September 1972.

In 1979 a single nestling remained in the Tower on 30 August; a meal from that day was compared with those sampled at infrequent intervals during the previous two months. This last meal was quite exceptional. Out of a total of 348 insects, 106 were beetles (Coleoptera), including 59 weevils and 34 rove-beetles. For comparison a meal taken in the first week of July contained just 19 coleopterans, of which 13 were ladybirds, out of a total of 898 insects; another sample, a week later, contained 5 coleopterans and 538 other insects; of two more meals taken in July and early August one, comprising 791 insects and spiders, contained only 7 coleopterans, while in the other there were no beetles at all in a total of 441 insects.

The name Coleoptera, literally 'sheath wings', refers to the modified front pair of wings, the elytra, usually horny or leathery, which encase the membranous hind wings used for flying. The success of the beetles as a group is due largely to the protection given by the tough elytra and the heavy cuticle covering the rest of the body; many coleopterans, weevils in particular, are so heavily armoured as to be almost indestructible. As food items they appear to be singularly unrewarding, for much of their weight is made up of unusable chitin. Faecal pellets taken from the swift nest-boxes contain the insoluble remains of the insects the birds have eaten and in many instances almost the entire thorax and head of a coleopteran can be identified, particularly if it is a rove-beetle or a weevil. So much of a beetle's body is excreted that is of no food value that in general it may be considered very poor fare compared with soft-bodied insects.

By August the insect population explosions characteristic of spring and high summer are over. The most nutritious insects, especially the aphids and the plant bugs which feed on the sap from young growing shoots and leaves, decline in numbers from a peak in June to a low in August, and not until late September do the numbers again rise to give a second peak. There is enough food for the swallows and martins to raise a second brood in late summer, but high in the air, where the swifts hunt for food, insects are much scarcer. This is reflected in the composition of the meals brought to the chicks late in the season. Too much should not be made of relatively few samples, as they are individually so variable, but it seems reasonable to infer from the high proportion of coleopterans in the meal taken on 30 August that the swift has to take such unrewarding fare because more nutritious insects are scarce at this time of the year. The departure of swifts earlier than swallows and martins is understandable when related to the different niches they occupy in the ecosystem.

7

In June 1976 one cloudless day followed another, the sun beating down with an intensity rarely experienced in Britain. Already, with no rain for weeks, the water levels in the reservoirs were dangerously low and the normally lush green countryside was tinged with an unaccustomed brown. In the Tower the heat was stifling; by mid-day the slates of the roof were too hot to touch and in the confined space under the roof, where no air circulates, the darkness enhanced the impression of being inside an oven. It was hot in the nest-boxes too, but at least there the air could circulate via the entrance hole, affording some relief to the chicks. We were not to know then that July was to become even hotter, with tragic consequences.

In the second half of June there were several instances of adults fighting in the nest-boxes, behaviour unprecedented so late in the season. Fighting in the spring, shortly after the birds first arrive, is quite common and may be attributed to rivalry over a mate or competition for a nest-box. David Lack records having seen about twenty fights, all except one occurring in May or early June before the eggs were laid; the one exception was on 13 July, when an adult with full food pouch, clearly without aggressive intent, entered a wrong nest-box by mistake and was attacked by the resident bird. When fights take place in the open air the two birds usually separate after a few seconds, but in the confines of a nest-box fights may last for several hours, the longest recorded by David Lack being 5¾ hours.

In 1976 fighting took place on at least three occasions when there were eggs or chicks in the nests, and there may well have been others, as we did not inspect all the nest-boxes every day. In the first instance, on 17 June, we found a swift lying dead near a nest containing two eggs. It was unmarked and there was no evident cause of death; as it was not carrying a leg-band we had no means of discovering if it was one of the resident pair or an intruder. The eggs in this nest later hatched, but on 1 July, when the box was again inspected, both chicks were lying outside the nest and had been dead for about two days. The presence in the nest-box of an ejected food bolus suggested that in this second instance a fight had taken place between one of the parents and an intruder, and the death of the chicks indicated that for some reason they had been abandoned.

On the third occasion a fight was already in progress in the nest-box of one of the two pairs being filmed, when I arrived at about 7.30 a.m. on the morning of 20 June. How long they had been fighting I had no means of knowing. Both birds were locked together beside the nest, eyes closed, each gripping the other with its sharp claws, one on its back resisting feebly, while the other pecked intermittently at its throat. The three young chicks lay very still in the nest itself. Even when the spotlamp was switched on for filming the birds carried on their fight, with eyes closed, oblivious to the light.

One is always loath to interfere when birds are behaving naturally, even when there is a risk of one being killed, but in this particular instance, with so much to lose if the chicks were to die, I decided to stop the fight after about half an hour. At first I tried to separate the two by inserting my hand and lifting off the bird on top, but as they were both fiercely clutching one another I merely raised both up together. Even in my hand they continued to peck one another and only when I worked my fingers in between them did they open their eyes and take in what was happening. The bird that had been supine released its grip, quickly shuffling to the entrance hole and dropping out. The second bird followed shortly afterwards and I was left

71

In 1976 the chicks
suffered horribly as
temperatures under
the slate roof rose
above 38° C (100° F)

wondering whether the shock of the fight, and my interference, would result in the chicks being abandoned. Fortunately within a few minutes one of the parents returned and brooded the chicks, and all was well, much to my relief. One can only speculate as to the identities of the contestants, but it may reasonably be assumed that one was a parent and the other an intruder.

Out-of-season fights such as these are so unusual that some explanation is called for. My own interpretation is that the intruders were young birds looking for nest sites for the first time and entering occupied nest-boxes by mistake and through inexperience. The reason why they were exploring for nest sites in late June, instead of in May or early June as is normal, is that these birds would probably not have become mature in the normal course of events until 1977. The summer of 1976 being so phenomenally hot, and food so abundant, some birds may have matured a season early, as a result of their unusually rich diet. Further evidence is provided by the fact that a few empty nest-boxes in the Tower were occupied for the first time in July, by pairs which each produced only a single egg. These hatched in the first week of August, at a time when the young swifts raised earlier in the year were already fully grown and about to leave for Africa. The late singletons were not fledged until September, but fortunately the good weather held until their departure.

This interpretation, if correct, suggests why immature swifts make the journey to Europe from Africa even though they will not breed; a rich diet, in successive years, may be necessary for the reproductive organs to mature, and this diet may only be available in northern temperate climates.

For the nestlings hatching normally in June, the month of July provided a superabundance of food but at the cost of being roasted alive day after day. Throughout Britain the countryside suffered badly in the worst drought in living memory. The ground cracked open, fields of corn ripened prematurely and once lush pastures shrivelled and turned brown. Horses and cattle sought out patches of shade wherever they could and every movement raised a cloud of dust where earlier they had stood in mud. Reservoirs dried completely, their muddy bottoms cracked open and baked hard like African salt-pans. The woodlands and hedgerows were blotched with the yellows and browns of dead leaves as trees succumbed to the drought, their skeletons later adding to those of the diseased elms.

In the Tower temperatures were even higher than in June, but we could at least escape the worst heat of the day, whereas the unfortunate nestlings were confined to the nest-boxes. They suffered horribly. In an attempt to lower their body temperatures they opened their beaks wide and panted, losing heat by passing air over the wet lining of the beak and throat. The sight of fat greyish-pink chicks, fluff pushing through the blotchy skin in patches, with naked scaly heads and a huge gape, panting into a pile of faecal pellets over the rim of the nest, must be one of the least attractive in Nature.

Until they are about two weeks old the chicks cannot move around the nest-box and are confined to the nest itself, but from then on they become more active and begin to exercise their wings, which at three weeks have sprouted their first quill feathers.

About the time when they first began to shuffle around the nest-box and flap their wings we became aware of tragedy. Chicks suddenly disappeared. Over a period of days nests under the south-facing roof of the Tower mysteriously emptied, and to our great chagrin this included one of the broods we were filming. We found the nestlings dead on the slates and in the gutters below the nest-boxes. This side of the Tower, hotter than the others, had become so unbearable that the chicks, able to move out of the nest for the first time, had scrambled to the nest entrance in search of cool air, and, still blind, had fallen to their deaths. It was sad to see their small bodies melting on the hot slates, attracting the blowflies, and an irony that birds

Overleaf: In the third week the long wing feathers break out of their blue sheaths

that had been fed on flies should now become food for flies.

But although the heat had fatal consequences for some, it guaranteed an abundance of insects for the survivors. Again and again the parent birds returned within the hour, sometimes with food pouches so distended that their beaks were agape, and the last insects caught could be seen struggling to escape from the sticky mass in the pouch. So satiated were some of the nestlings that the parents found difficulty in stimulating them to take in yet another meal.

The eyes open at about the time that the wing feathers break out of their blue sheaths, and for the first time the young swifts become aware of their surroundings. Now they actively greet the arrival of the parent pleading for food with their piping cries. At the age of a month the wings and tail are grown sufficiently for the young bird to preen its feathers and exercise, by wing stretching and doing 'press-ups', raising its body off the floor with wings and tail extended. Such limited exercises are all that are possible in the confines of the nest-box.

For a few days after the eyes open the young swifts are as unprepossessing as ever, their fat bodies prickly with quills. But then as the birds lose weight and feathers cover them their appearance changes. Almost overnight, it seems, they undergo a kind of metamorphosis, from ugly fledgeling to beautiful young swift. As more and more feathers come through and the wings lengthen, the young birds begin to resemble their parents. At this age they are very active, exercising their wings and shuffling around the nest-box a great deal. Their appetites are undiminished and they make great demands on the parents, harassing them with their continuous pleading for food even when, as in 1976, it is abundant. In 1977 we were to see a quite different, but much more normal situation; adults returning after hours flying

Left: On cold, wet days the parent swifts return exhausted, feathers soaked and furrowed by wind and rain, too tired even to feed their offspring

Right: The arrangement of feathers around the gape shown by this three-week-old fledgling could be to direct the airflow when catching insects at speed

Their fat bodies prickly with
emerging feathers, nestling
swifts are at their least attractive
in their second and third weeks

As their feathers grow and
wings lengthen young swifts
seem to undergo a
metamorphosis; at six weeks
they are ready to fly

through driving rain, feathers soaked and plumage furrowed by the impact of countless raindrops, and so cold and exhausted that they lay for several minutes on the floor of the nest-box with eyes closed, before summoning the strength to feed their importunate young.

Before they leave the nest numbered rings are placed on the legs of the young swifts in the Tower, to identify them in later years. The practice of bird-ringing has grown enormously and every year hundreds of thousands of birds are caught, ringed and released in many parts of the world, by amateur and professional ornithologists. If birds carrying rings are re-captured, or are killed or found dead, the finder is asked to return the ring, or record its number, with details of locality, date and circumstances in which the bird was found. In this way a picture is built up of the life stories of particular species, including factors which may have brought about changes in their numbers and distribution. Identifying individual birds adds very considerably to the quality of the data acquired when studying migration, in particular, but inevitably the number of rings returned is small. The success of ringing programmes depends on large numbers of birds being captured initially, and of course on the conscientiousness of those who later find the ringed birds in making returns. Migrant birds are especially difficult subjects for study because many travel immense distances, over the sea or inhospitable terrain, where the chances of finding their corpses are very poor, and the return of a ring even less likely. Birds recognize no political boundaries in their migrations and collaboration between countries is essential for bird-ringing to be successful.

In Britain rings are issued only by the British Trust for Ornithology to authorized bird-ringers, who must be properly trained in the techniques of capturing and handling birds. If they ring nestlings their permit must also carry a 'Pullus' (the name given a nestling or a chick not yet flying) endorsement. Each year in Britain well over 600,000 birds of some 300 species are ringed by more than 2000 field ornithologists working individually or in

An adult swift carrying a ring issued by the British Trust for Ornithology

groups. The rings are designed to fit the legs of particular species; each is numbered and carries the message 'Inform British Museum London'.

In Oxford, swifts were first ringed in the Tower in the late 1940s, but the ringing of nesting adults was discontinued when it was realized that the disturbance could cause the birds to desert. Adults are now ringed only if they can be captured while resting in the nest-boxes as non-breeders, or as parents caught in the nest after their young have flown. Of recent years effort has been concentrated on the pulli, and Roy Overall, who began ringing swifts in the Tower in 1962 and has recorded the success or failure of every pair of breeding birds since then, had ringed 734 pulli and 51 adults by the end of the 1979 season. Roy it was who found the swift which holds the record for longevity dying in the Tower. Ringed as adult D 3082 in

The indigo eye of this five-week-old fledgling will turn to brown in the adult, and the white head feathers will be lost

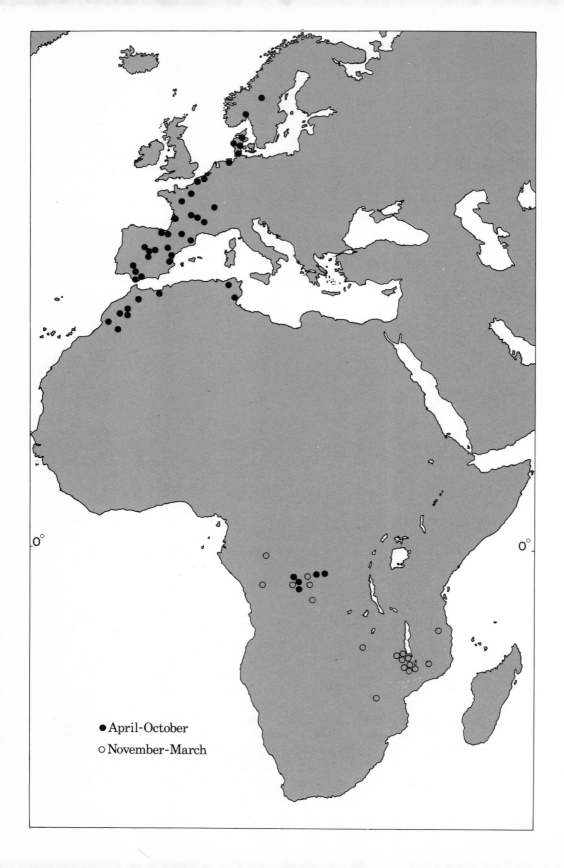

● April–October
○ November–March

nest-box E3 in the Tower on 29 June 1948, it was first controlled, i.e., re-captured, recorded and released, breeding in box N3 in July 1958, and again in August 1960, breeding in the same nest-box; it died in the Tower on 22 June 1964, when it must have been at least 18 years old.

In the whole of Britain 105,838 swifts had been ringed up to the end of 1978, and of these 2224 have been recovered, a recovery rate of 2.1 per cent. (The figure for the mute swan for comparison is 34.8 per cent.) Most of these recoveries have been in the United Kingdom, and only sixty-three birds have so far been recovered in other countries of Europe and Africa. Few though they are, these records of foreign recoveries are of special interest, since they tell us something of the distribution of swifts ringed in Britain, not only during the summer but throughout the year. The map on page 82 includes all the reliable reports of swifts which were ringed in Britain and recovered in Europe and Africa between 1957 and 1978. Although the number of birds involved is small it is possible to group the recoveries in relation to the time of year and the countries in which the birds were recovered.

The first group includes all those recovered in the summer months from May to September, in countries of northern Europe – Norway, Sweden, Denmark, the Netherlands, Germany and France. All except two of these swifts had been ringed as adults and so could have been breeding birds within range of their nesting sites, or non-breeders roaming Europe in response to weather movements. The two exceptions were both ringed as pulli. One, which left its nest in Kent on 29 July 1958, was found dead in the Netherlands five days later, presumably on its way to Africa. The other, ringed in the Oxford Tower on 7 July 1951, met its death in spectacular fashion a year later by being sucked into the air intake of a jet engine of a plane flying over Jutland in Denmark, 800 kilometres (500 miles) to the northeast.

The second group includes the thirteen birds recovered in Spain. Of these, two were re-covered in May, eight in August, two in September and one in October. All except one

had been ringed as adults, the exception being a bird which left its nest in the Oxford Tower on 31 July 1958 and was recovered three days later at Puente de Vallecas, near Madrid, 1300 kilometres (810 miles) away *en route* to Africa. Spain appears to be the country through which swifts ringed in Britain pass on their spring and autumn migrations, 62 per cent of all recoveries being made in August.

The third group includes birds recovered in North Africa between April and September; seven in Morocco and two in Tunisia. Two of these birds were recovered in Morocco in June and July, six and eight years after being ringed in Britain as adults, suggesting that North Africa is not only on the migration route to the swifts' winter quarters in southern Africa but is also one of the localities where adult swifts spend the summer when not breeding.

South of Morocco there is a huge gap in the records, for no swift ringed in Britain has been found in the vast expanse of Africa between Morocco and Zaire.

In the fourth group are the eleven swifts recovered in Zaire in the months of January, February, April, May, June, September and November. Zaire is evidently where some of our swifts spend the winter, but again, as in Morocco, adult birds of breeding age have been recovered in summer when one would have expected them to be nesting in Europe. One of these birds, ringed as an adult in Hertford in July 1966, achieved distinction by being shot in Zaire with a bow and arrow, in June 1968.

The fifth and last group includes birds recovered only in the winter months, from November to March, all in countries south of Latitude 10° S; eight in Malawi, and one each in Tanzania, Zambia, Mozambique and Zimbabwe-Rhodesia. These countries are at the southerly limit of the swifts' migration, and to date no birds have been found there in the summer months between April and October.

The single record of a ringed bird found in Zambia is of particular personal interest. Having compiled the records of all swifts ringed in Britain and recovered elsewhere, I had occasion to visit Zambia in October 1979. My

Map showing foreign recoveries of British swifts, 1957–78

first day was spent in the company of Colin and Freda Heygate, who own a farm near Kitwe and are both keen naturalists. That day the flying ants were swarming in enormous numbers and being taken by swifts of several species, possibly including our common swift. I mentioned the single recovery of a ringed European swift in Zambia and by the most extraordinary coincidence found that it had been Colin and Freda Heygate who had found it and arranged for the ring to be returned to the British Trust for Ornithology. The circumstances add to our very meagre knowledge of how swifts may meet their deaths. In November 1976 a storm of great intensity passed over the farm, accompanied by localized turbulent winds and a tremendous downpour. Even where tropical storms are common it was exceptionally sudden and intense. At its height Colin went outside to see to the welfare of the animals. In the yard he found several swifts floundering helplessly, beaten into the mud by the torrential rain. Collecting them up, he carried them inside and by the following morning they were dried out and recovered. All were local swifts except one, which carried a ring placed on its leg as a fledgling in Lancashire in June 1969. All the birds were later released and flew away none the worse for their experience, owing their lives to their discovery and rescue with perhaps minutes left to live, and against all the odds. Sudden tropical storms may now be added to the list of hazards which may bring swifts down and so cause their deaths, along with cold, starvation, telephone wires, jet engines, mass slaughterers of small birds in countries bordering the Mediterranean, cats, rats, hobbies, owls, peregrines and, in one instance that must be unique, a bow and arrow.

The records of nestlings ringed in Britain show that, with but few exceptions, recoveries are made within a relatively short distance of where they were ringed. Even though the fledgling swift leaves almost immediately for Africa, with little time for orientation, it has an extraordinary ability to return to the locality where it was reared. However, few of these birds actually return to the same nesting site to breed. Of 621 pulli ringed in the Oxford Tower between 1956 and 1966, only eight were recaptured there in the decade 1958 to 1968, and not a single bird in the years since then (although because so few adults are handled some mature birds ringed as pulli in the Tower may have returned undetected).

As year by year data from ringed swifts accumulate, an outline of the pattern of their lives emerges. The young birds depart for Africa within a day or so of leaving the nest, travelling via Spain and North Africa, and reaching Zaire by November. The route they take down the length of Africa is unknown. During the winter they drift across the countries of southeast Africa, and in March they begin their spring migration northwards, arriving in Europe in May. Although they may return to the general locality of their birth they roam the skies over the length and breadth of Europe during the summer, their movements dictated by the weather. In the autumn they fly to Africa, returning again next spring. In their second year they may make perfunctory attempts at finding a nest site and even building a nest, landing briefly for the first time. Some immature birds may not return to Europe every year, but remain in Africa during the summer. Those that do make the journey to Europe may do so not only for the rich diet, which they probably need if their gonads are to develop, but also to establish in their memories the locations of nest sites to which they may later return to breed. An explanation for the behaviour of screaming parties of swifts could be that they include immature birds locating established colonies by banging at the nest entrances, screaming at the breeding birds on their nests and being replied to in kind. As three-year-olds, returning again to Europe, they may even find mates, make nests and lay eggs, though the eggs will be sterile. Not until their fourth year are they successful in laying fertile eggs and raising young. Having settled on a nest site they then return to it again and again in subsequent years, even to the same nest and with the same mate. But it would seem that some summers they do not return; instead they miss a season, and stay in Africa.

A fully fledged young swift; in flight its white face distinguishes it from the adult

8

In the last days before it leaves the nest the young swift is at its most beautiful. Its long, pointed wings are fully grown, the primary feathers edged with white. Throat and forehead are predominantly white, and it is this feature alone which later distinguishes the young birds from the adults when they are flying together. The deep-set eyes, shielded against the friction of the wind under heavy brows, are at first a deep indigo; later the iris becomes dark brown, as in the adult.

Unlike song-birds of similar size, whose departure from the nest varies by only a few days, the age at which a young swift is ready to leave may vary by as much as three weeks, depending on the weather when it is a nestling. The average age at which Oxford swifts leave is about six weeks, but in bad summers this may be extended to as much as eight weeks.

In the last week, the young swift sits near the entrance hole looking out for most of the day. Occasionally it shuffles around the nest-box, doing 'press-ups' and wing-stretching, but always returning to the hole as though drawn by a magnet.

From below the Tower one can look up at the nest-boxes in the base of the flutes, and see white faces peering down from the entrance holes as the young swifts look out on the world to which they will soon commit themselves. For each one the countdown has begun, the internal clock in its brain ticking away the days, then the hours, minutes and seconds until the very moment when instinct determines that it must plunge into space.

As we watched and waited for what was to be for us the climax of the film and for the birds the first major crisis in their lives, an air of excitement pervaded the Tower. This was particularly noticeable in the mornings.

First flight of a young swift; it may remain airborne for the next three years

In the last days of July white-faced young
swifts peer down from the nest holes in
the flutes

Throughout the summer the birds that had stayed all night on the wing had come down to the Tower each morning for their usual display of aerobatics and to scream and be screamed at by those nesting in the Tower, but as the time came for the young birds to leave it seemed that an element of excitement had been added to the general air of *joie de vivre*. This excitement was shared by the swifts inside and outside the Tower, and communicated itself to us, too. Now, in the mornings, the parties of screamers would fly close to where the young birds were looking out, and often several would follow one another up to the entrance hole itself. Occasionally one would cling on to the slate roof for a few seconds before tumbling off to join the others in another circuit. As the days went by birds with white faces could be seen among those flying round the Tower in the mornings, youngsters which had already flown and which seemed to be screaming encouragement to those still inside to come out and join them.

It was no less exciting for us inside the Tower, waiting to capture on film the actual moment of departure of the birds we had watched for so long. Of the two nests over which we had set up our cameras at the beginning of May, one brood had been lost entirely when both nestlings had fallen from the entrance in the unbearable July heat. The other, with three chicks, had survived the trauma of a fight, with the attendant risk of desertion, but one nestling later fell to its death. By the end of July the two surviving birds were ready to leave. Curiously, although they had been conditioned to artificial light from the time they hatched, and had always disregarded it, in the week before they left the brightness in the nest-box caused them increasing unease. Perhaps with a greater awareness of their surroundings the unnatural light was disturbing, or it may merely have been an additional element heightening their excitability as the time for their departure drew nearer.

Watching them as they sat looking out of the entrance hole for hours at a time, one could not help wondering what was going on in their brains. It was tempting, even though scientifically quite improper, to ascribe to them a prescience of the life they were to lead, after their first momentous drop out of the nest hole. Until then the boundary of their world had been the nest-box itself, their view of what lay outside restricted to a two-inch hole overhanging a steep roof. All their lives they had been fed by their parents, yet from the instant they left the nest they would have to fend for themselves. Unlike the young of song-birds, which are fed by their parents for some time after leaving the nest, the young swift is immediately independent. Nor are there any practice flights, giving time for muscles and sinews to strengthen, and the coordination between brain and wing to become perfect. Although its only preparation for a life in the air has been the limited exercises possible in the nest-box, the young swift must fly perfectly from the moment it first spreads its wings; and not only fly and feed itself, but leave almost immediately on the long journey to Africa, ahead of its parents.

Little wonder that, as the time approaches for the young swifts to leave, instinct and fear are in conflict. Twice one morning, between 7.30 and 8 a.m., when the screams of the swifts outside the Tower seemed most insistent, one of our two young birds tipped forward into the nest hole, as if to leave, but quickly changed its mind when its head was out of the hole and scrambled back again in fright. The next morning there were three birds in the nest-box when we arrived; an adult sitting in the nest itself and the two young birds near the nest entrance. This time, when the lights were switched on, the adult slipped out and was followed immediately and without any hesitation by one of the young birds.

For the younger bird left behind, the countdown was to continue for three more days. For much of the time it seemed content to sit at the entrance, occasionally exercising and stretching its wings, and being fed at more frequent intervals now that it did not have to share meals with its elder sibling. Each morning it seemed that the time had come for it to leave, but every time it tilted forward into the nest hole it became very frightened and scrambled back again, with much fluffing of feathers and rapid breathing, followed by more wing stretching. On the second morning it scared itself badly when its feet fell through the hole and it was supported across the entrance by its breast and tail, and this ended any further attempts to leave that day.

It left at last on the morning of the third day, but not without a final moment of panic. At about eight o'clock it tipped forward into the nest hole and this time went too far to turn back. With most of its body outside it clung upside down by one foot, a wing tip braced across the entrance. From outside we could see it make an attempt to return to the safety of the nest, but there was no turning back and after a few seconds it let go and plummeted into space.

It is very probable that we were responsible for the undignified and quite atypical departure of this young swift. Perhaps the internal clock which determines precisely when instinct shall win over fear had a few more minutes to run, and we precipitated events with our lights and cameras. Be that as it may, once it had taken to the air its flight was indistinguishable from that of all the other swifts and in seconds it was lost among the excited birds screaming around the Tower.

In the mornings there is great excitement as swifts scream and fly close to the nest holes where the young birds are waiting to leave

Inset: The moment of departure

In the days that followed other young swifts of similar age left the nests one by one, leaving only a few single birds from late broods. Every morning the air was filled with excited screaming and, standing on the Museum roof below the Tower, one instinctively ducked one's head as a party of black crescent-winged birds, many now with white faces, dived out of a blue sky at speed, with a sound like a flight of arrows as their wings cut through the air. In the evenings large flocks of swifts assembled above the towers and spires of Oxford, their screams growing fainter as they rose higher and higher until lost to sight.

The memory of one particular evening in August will always remain with me. I was attending an open-air performance of *The Taming of the Shrew* in the gardens of Keble College, close by the Tower. It was a warm, still evening and as the shadows lengthened the stage lights were switched on to illuminate the players and musicians beneath a huge beech tree. In the Induction, Scene 2, when the drunken tailor, Sly, is being persuaded that he is in fact a noble Lord I suddenly became aware of the penetrating screams of swifts. High over the already darkened gardens a large flock was wheeling and darting, wings glinting in the last rays of the setting sun. Sly is asked, 'Wilt thou have music? hark! Apollo plays, and twenty caged nightingales do sing.' No nightingales, and certainly not caged, the response from the

swifts was a faint chorus of screams as they drifted away to the south, until they became invisible against the darkening sky.

Within a few days the swifts were gone, leaving only a few stragglers with late broods. Somewhere over Europe, beginning their long journey to South Africa, were our two special swifts, those we had watched for so many hours, from the time they hatched as naked, pink monstrosities to the moment when, as beautiful young birds, they committed themselves to an aerial existence uniquely theirs, for which they are so marvellously adapted.

In the years ahead how many hundreds of thousands of miles will they fly? How many wingbeats, flying day and night, the last to see the sun setting in the west as they rise high above the dark earth, and the first to catch the earliest rays at sunrise in the mornings? What will they see in their travels, crossing continents, sea, mountain, jungle and desert, roaming half the world in their search for insects.

Will we ever see them again? In 1977 they may have returned, and again in the summers following, though we have had no way of knowing whether they were among those screaming round the Tower. Not until 1980 will we have the opportunity of finding out if they have come back, this time to raise their own families, for then we may be able to read the rings on the legs of the nesting birds, and perhaps meet again.

Index

Photograph Credits

(the numerals refer to page numbers)

Tony Allen: 8/9, 11 *(left)*, 21 *(bottom)*, 26/7, 34, 35, 42/3, 46 *(bottom)*, 47, 55, 58/9, 68, 78 *(bottom)*, 81, 88, 92

Tony Allen/Derek Bromhall: back cover, 6/7, 24, 36, 40/1

Heather Angel: 21 *(top)*

Ron Austin/F. W. Lane: 20 *(colour)*

S. C. Bisserot/Bruce Coleman Ltd: 19 *(top left)*

Clive Bromhall: front cover, 2, 38/39, 42 *(bottom)*, 43 *(bottom)*, 44/5, 46 *(top)*, 49, 50 *(insects)*, 51 *(left)*, 53, 56, 58 *(top)*, 61, 62, 65 *(colour)*, 66 *(left, top)*, 67 *(top right, bottom)*, 70, 72, 74/5, 76, 77, 78 *(top, left)*, 79, 80, 84

Derek Bromhall: 10, 12, 18 *(bw)*, 19 *(bottom right)*, 32, 33, 50, 51 *(right)*, 60/1, 66 *(bottom)*, 67 *(top left)*, 78 *(centre)*, 86/7, 90/1

Arthur Brook/The National Museum of Wales: 1, 65 *(bw)*

R. Carr/Bruce Coleman Ltd: 29 *(colour)*

Stephen Dalton/Natural History Photographic Agency: 31 *(colour)*

Treat Davidson/F. W. Lane: 20 *(bw)*

David Dickie: 63

P. Ginn/F. W. Lane: 18 *(colour)*

Eric and David Hosking: 28, 29 *(bw)*, 30/1 *(bw)*

Elaine Hurrell: 11 *(right)*

E. A. Janes/Natural History Photographic Agency: 30 *(colour)*

Chris Mead: 22, 23

Loren A. McIntyre/International Wildlife Magazine: 14, 17

Mike Price/Bruce Coleman Ltd: 19 *(top right)*

Dr de Zylva/F. W. Lane: 19 *(bottom left)*

Hutchinson & Co. (Publishers) Ltd

An imprint of the Hutchinson Publishing Group

3 Fitzroy Square, London W1P 6JD

Hutchinson Group (Australia) Pty Ltd
30–32 Cremorne Street, Richmond South, Victoria 3121
PO Box 151, Broadway, New South Wales 2007

Hutchinson Group (NZ) Ltd
32–34 View Road, PO Box 40–086, Glenfield, Auckland 10

Hutchinson Group (SA) (Pty) Ltd
PO Box 337, Bergvlei 2012, South Africa

First published 1980

© Derek Bromhall 1980

Set in Monophoto Ehrhardt

Printed and bound in Great Britain by
Morrison & Gibb Ltd, London and Edinburgh

British Library CIP Data
Bromhall, Derek
Devil birds.
1. Swifts
I. Title
598.8'99   QL696.A552

ISBN 0 09 141730 9 (cased)
ISBN 0 09 141731 7 (paper)